Date Due

MAR 3 '58			
SEP 13 '65			
OCT 4 '65			
MAY 6			
MAY 6 '66			
SEP 19 '69			
OCT 23 '72			
OCT 29 '86			
	PRINTED	IN U. S. A.	

THE TECHNIQUE OF
STAGE LIGHTING

COLOURED SHADOWS

A striking and beautiful stage effect: the shadows on the background are in all the colours
of the spectrum, while the dancers are illuminated in a soft, white light.

Frontispiece

THE TECHNIQUE OF STAGE LIGHTING

By

ROLLO GILLESPIE WILLIAMS, F.I.E.S.

LONDON
SIR ISAAC PITMAN & SONS, LTD.

First published 1947
Revised and reprinted 1952

SIR ISAAC PITMAN & SONS, Ltd.
PITMAN HOUSE, PARKER STREET, KINGSWAY, LONDON, W.C.2
THE PITMAN PRESS, BATH
PITMAN HOUSE, LITTLE COLLINS STREET, MELBOURNE
27 BECKETTS BUILDINGS, PRESIDENT STREET, JOHANNESBURG

ASSOCIATED COMPANIES
PITMAN PUBLISHING CORPORATION
2 WEST 45TH STREET, NEW YORK

SIR ISAAC PITMAN & SONS (CANADA), Ltd.
(INCORPORATING THE COMMERCIAL TEXT BOOK COMPANY)
PITMAN HOUSE, 381–383 CHURCH STREET, TORONTO

MADE IN GREAT BRITAIN AT THE PITMAN PRESS, BATH
E2—(G.290)

FOREWORD

SOME twenty odd years ago the entertainment world was startled by a scientific invention that revolutionized the film industry—the photographing of sound. The result of this amazing development enabled the little man, living in some small remote country town or in one of the suburbs of a big city, to see and hear the performance of an international star. The modern talking picture has undoubtedly reached a very high standard of perfection.

An equally marvellous invention has enabled the same little man to sit at home and by twisting a knob on his radio set, to tune in to more or less whatever he wants to hear, and even now, if he is able to purchase the apparatus, he can both see and hear a programme of television.

During the same period, what has been done to help the stage? The theatre of to-day from a technical point of view has been sadly neglected. Admittedly a crude attempt has been made to amplify the voice of the artist but in many cases this rather clumsy device is resented by the public.

The question naturally arises: can modern science improve stage production? It seems incredible that, in spite of the advance made by science in every direction, the producer of a stage play has to fall back on painted canvas stretched on a wooden frame for his scenery surroundings. This method of décor and background has been in existence for generations and very little advance has been made in the illumination of these scenic effects. Whereas in the old days oil lamps were used in the " footlights," followed by gas-jets, to-day we possess a row of gas-filled lamps in a series of metal cases. In the " flys " above we have a similar equipment with the addition of a few directional lamps.

On each side of the stage, flood lamps and directional spotlights are occasionally supplied, with two or three arc lamps from the front of the house, and this comprises the average equipment of a West End theatre.

If the same amount of brain power that has been concentrated on talking pictures and radio had been concentrated on the theatre, it can be assumed that stage scenery would be a matter of projecting coloured pictures through translucent screens, which would mean an immense saving of time and labour, and consequently a reduction in expense.

As far as the more spectacular type of stage show is concerned, science can be of the greatest assistance, and the answer to the whole thing is " lighting." There are infinite possibilities in this direction. Stage lighting is still in its infancy, and it is now up to the enterprising producer to exploit it to the full.

Mr. Gillespie Williams has produced a valuable textbook on this subject and it should prove a very practical contribution to the technical improvement of stage production.

Jack Hulbert

35 *Curzon Street,*
Mayfair,
*London, W.*1.

PREFACE

MANY times during the last few years I have been impressed with the need for a textbook on stage lighting that will meet the varying needs of the many people who are concerned with it, and more especially of those who wish to gain ideas concerning the artistic use of illumination on the stage.

Stage lighting is a subject that covers a very large field, and the expert must have knowledge of the scientific, artistic, and engineering facts that underlie it. To enable the reader—whether he is stage producer, lighting expert, architect, artist, engineer, or contractor—to find quickly the section he specifically requires, I have divided this book into four parts.

The first part, entitled "Scientific Basis," gives important information concerning vision, colour, and the science of illumination. The chapter entitled "Vision and Colour," in particular, deals with scientific facts, a knowledge of which is most important to any one concerned with the *use* of stage lighting.

The architect, engineer, and contractor engaged on the design and lay-out of stage lighting installations may be primarily interested in Part II, "The Adaptation and Control of Light," which includes five chapters dealing with stage lighting and control apparatus, also its lay-out and installation.

Applied stage illumination is both a science and an art, and in Part III I have endeavoured to outline some principles for the effective use of light and colour in building up artistic lighting compositions. Whereas the scientific facts stated in Part I are firmly established and widely accepted, much less is generally known about the principles of light and colour in an artistic sense, and much of the information given in Part III is based upon my own researches and practical experience—which cover a period of more than twenty years. It is always difficult to lay down hard and fast rules concerning artistic matters; and while endeavouring not to dogmatize, I hope that the information and ideas presented in the four chapters of Part III will be of some assistance to those engaged in the fascinating study of applied stage lighting.

In the course of my life I have several times been persuaded to help out amateur dramatic and operatic societies by looking after the lighting of their shows, and I am familiar with the problems that beset those who wish to provide some effective lighting but have access to the hall only a few hours before the dress rehearsal, and have to rely largely on the existing lighting installation. The harassed lighting man, struggling with this limited equipment, will, it is hoped, gain some new ideas as to what can be done with the outfit at his disposal. Part IV, entitled "Practical Lighting for Stage Productions," has the amateur enthusiast well in mind, though the author hopes that professional producers, with their wider range of equipment, will also find this section of major interest, as it is based on many years of research and experiment.

Recently I have had occasion to spend some time in America in connection with Theatre Lighting. This book has been written primarily to deal with British practice, but almost all of Parts I and III apply to practice on both sides of the Atlantic. Certain chapters in Parts II and IV, dealing with apparatus, colour filters, lay-out and installation, should be read as descriptions of British practice. In America the main difference is that higher lighting intensities are often employed, and spotlights are used to a greater extent for building up the general lighting.

In conclusion, I should like to express my gratitude and appreciation to Mr. F. W. Bartrum of Nottingham, for providing the many line and coloured drawings that appear in the illustrations; also to Messrs. R. R. Beard, Ltd., Messrs. Blackburn, Starling & Co., Ltd., Messrs. W. J. Furse & Co., Ltd., and the Major Equipment Co., Ltd., for allowing photographs of their apparatus to be reproduced. I should like to thank Dr. S. English, D.Sc., M.I.E.E., F.Inst.P., for his kindness in reading proofs of Chapters 1 and 2. My thanks are also warmly given to Messrs. Jack Hulbert, Dennis Astell, J. Brandon-Thomas, W. Bailey, W. Belcher, A. S. Hackman, Charles Henry, George Thomas, and Miss N. Gibson, and many others, for their encouragement and assistance on many occasions: and to the four authors and publishers to whom acknowledgment is made in the text. Last, but not least, I wish to thank my wife Catherine for suggesting the book in the first place and for tolerating me in the period during which it was written.   R. G. W.

NOTE TO THE SECOND IMPRESSION

RAPID technical developments in the last few years in the fields of lamp engineering and control devices have provided the theatre with important new tools for the theatre lighting craftsman. In this second impression I have endeavoured to bring up to date Chapters 3, 4, 5, and 7 which deal with these subjects. I am indebted to Herbert Kliegl and James F. Gibbings for their assistance and to the Color Lighting Corporation of America for the loan of photographs of the Rollocolor system.   R. G. W.

CONTENTS

CONTENTS

ILLUSTRATIONS

COLOUR PLATES

PART I. SCIENTIFIC BASIS

■

CHAPTER I

VISION AND COLOUR

THERE is no such thing as simple white light. What appears to be white light is found, upon examination, to be a combination of certain hues of coloured light. These hues are seen in the rainbow, which is, in fact, a spectrum of white light, and shows the separate colours that compose it.

THE VISIBLE SPECTRUM

The word *Light*, as commonly employed, has two distinct meanings—

(*a*) Radiant energy, which, by its action upon the eye, enables vision to take place.

(*b*) The sensations in the eye: i.e. the images of light and colour that are perceived.

In this book, we are concerned more with light as a phenomenon than as radiant energy, but when discussing the technicalities of illumination it is well to keep in mind the different aspects of light, as radiation and as physiological effect. As radiant energy, light travels through the ether in the form of waves, at the rate of 186,300 miles per second. The wave-lengths of radiant energy vary over a very large range; but when considering vision, we need concern ourselves only with that band of wave-lengths known as the visible spectrum, extending from approximately 0·39 to 0·76 Microns. (See page 2 and Fig. 1, page 4.)

Sir Isaac Newton discovered that a beam of sunlight, passed through a glass prism, is refracted so that the light beam is broken up into a continuous band of different colours, like the rainbow. There is a large number of colour hues corresponding to different wave-lengths of light in the visible spectrum, but Sir Isaac Newton arbitrarily named seven: red, orange, yellow, green, blue, indigo, and violet, no doubt choosing those that, to him, were most conspicuous. This has led many people to assume that the spectrum comprises only seven colours, and, furthermore, to endeavour to prove a physical relationship between "the seven colours of the spectrum" and the seven notes of a musical octave. Actually, over 120 different hues can be detected in the visible spectrum of light, and, under suitable viewing conditions, it is possible to see an even greater number. The writer generally works on the basis of fourteen colour hues in the ordinary spectrum of white light, these being—

RED	GREEN
ORANGE	BLUISH-GREEN
ORANGE-YELLOW	PEACOCK BLUE
YELLOW	GREENISH-BLUE
LEMON	TURQUOISE
YELLOW-GREEN	BLUE
APPLE-GREEN	VIOLET

N.B. The visible spectrum, however, does not include the family of purples, i.e. mauve, cerise, magenta, crimson, etc. But as these colour hues are perceived just as clearly by the eye as the actual spectral colours, they can be added to the list just given, thus forming a complete list of fundamental colours with which vision is concerned.

The wave-lengths of light are measured in terms of the Ångström Unit (Symbol Å.U.) = $1/10,000,000$ mm., or the Milli-Micron (Symbol M.μ.) = $1/1,000,000$ mm., or in terms of the Micron (Symbol μ) = $1/1,000$ mm. The wave-lengths corresponding to the visible spectrum represent only a very small portion of radiant energy, and correspond to 3900–7600 Å.U. (or 0·39 to 0·76 μ . . .). These, together with the infra-red rays (a continuance beyond the red end of the visible spectrum) and ultra-violet rays (a continuance beyond the violet end of the spectrum), constitute what is commonly termed light. Strictly speaking, however, ultra-violet and infra-red rays are not light, since they excite no visual response in the eye.

COLOUR VISION

Vision takes place because radiations from a light source enter the eye of the onlooker. Light rays travel in straight lines and may either proceed directly from the light source into the eye or fall upon objects that reflect them into the eye. The onlooker, therefore, is conscious of an image of light: in the former case he would receive an image of the light source, and in the latter case an image of the objects. It is important to realize that when viewing persons and things we are conscious only of images of light, and that visually these persons and objects are acting as reflectors, causing light rays to be reflected into our eyes, where they are focused into images.

An object seen to be white in daylight reflects all the light rays comprising the visible spectrum; but when an object appears to be coloured, then it selectively reflects only certain colours of this light, and absorbs the remainder.

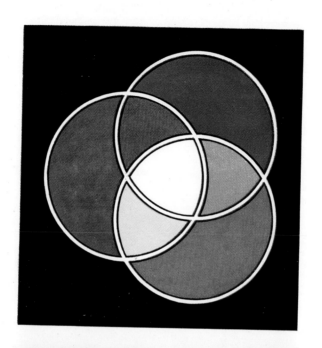

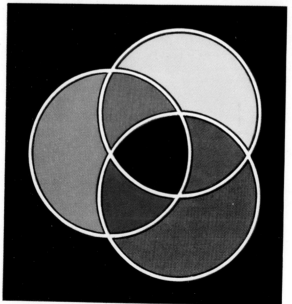

PLATE I
(*Above*) THE ADDITIVE METHOD OF MIXING COLOURS
(*Below*) THE SUBTRACTIVE METHOD OF MIXING COLOURS

According to the Young-Helmholtz theory, vision depends upon the action of three independent physiological processes, involving three sets of nerves. All the colours of the spectrum (together with the purples, which are not in the spectrum) can be matched in hue by mixing light corresponding to three monochromatic primary colours, red, green, and blue, in proper proportions, and white itself can be produced by a suitable mixture of these three primaries. The Young-Helmholtz theory assumes that each of the three sets of nerves corresponds to, and is stimulated by, one of the primary colours, red, green, or blue. Thus, when white is perceived, red, green, and blue lights are being simultaneously received by the eye and all three sets of nerves are being actuated, causing the onlooker to behold the phenomenon of white. When the red and green nerve sets are stimulated, the resultant phenomenon appears to be yellow; while mauve and peacock blue are the result of equal stimulation of the red and blue sets and of the green and blue sets respectively. When the stimuli are not equal in strength, then other colour hues are perceived, as, for example, violet, when the blue stimulus is strong and the red stimulus weak.

THE ADDITIVE METHOD OF MIXING COLOURS

Monochromatic Red, Green, and Blue are regarded as the primary colours of light, since by suitable mixtures of these any known colour hues can be matched, as will be seen from the following examples—

Red plus Green plus Blue Light *produces*	White Light
Red plus one-half Green Light *produces*	Orange Light
Red plus Green Light	*produces* Yellow Light
Blue plus Green Light	*produces* Peacock Blue Light
Blue plus one-half Red Light	*produces* Cerise Light
Blue plus Red Light	*produces* Magenta Light

The production of colours by mixing the primaries of light—red, green, and blue—is called the Additive Method of Colour Mixture. The eye is a synthetic rather than an analytical instrument, and when it is simultaneously stimulated by light rays of different colours, the result is additive, and the different colours do not neutralize each other in any way. Plate I shows the primary colours, red, green, and blue, and where they overlap in pairs there are seen the secondary colours, yellow, magenta, and peacock blue, while white is seen in the centre, where all three primaries overlap.

The Maxwell Colour Triangle (Fig. 2) further illustrates the tri-colour method of colour mixing. It is assumed that at RED, GREEN, and BLUE are light sources providing red, green, and blue light,

3

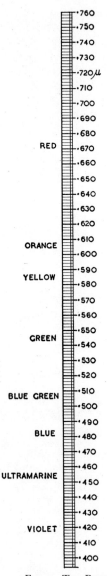

·760
·750
·740
·730
·720μ
·710
·700
·690
·680
RED ·670
·660
·650
·640
·630
·620
·610
ORANGE ·600
·590
YELLOW ·580
·570
·560
·550
GREEN ·540
·530
·520
·510
BLUE GREEN ·500
·490
·480
BLUE ·470
·460
ULTRAMARINE ·450
·440
·430
VIOLET ·420
·410
·400

FIG. I. THE RANGE IN MICRONS OF THE VISIBLE SPECTRUM SHOWING THE WAVE-LENGTHS OF CERTAIN COLOURS

which diminish in strength proportionately to the distance between any one light source and the opposite base line (it being assumed that the illumination has then reached vanishing point). Thus, green light is represented to be at full strength at the top corner and diminishes until along the line RED/BLUE it has zero intensity, the decrease in illumination being proportional to the distance from the top corner. Similarly, the red light from the right-hand bottom corner diminishes to vanishing point along GREEN/BLUE and the blue light from the remaining corner along GREEN/RED.

The relative intensities of the red, the green, and the blue lights necessary to produce white light are represented by the co-ordinates of the point W, where all three meet at an equal distance from RED, GREEN, and BLUE. It will then be seen that along the three sides of the triangle we get every colour hue produced by the mixture of each pair of primary colours. Thus, along the line GREEN/RED is every possible mixture of these two colours, with pure green and pure red at the ends of the line. Half-way along GREEN/RED there are equal proportions of red and green light, giving yellow light; and at other points along the line GREEN/RED are found orange, yellow, yellow-green, and so on. Half-way along the line GREEN/BLUE is peacock blue, and other colours along that line are turquoise, bluish-green, and so on. The line BLUE/RED includes violet, cerise, magenta, crimson, etc., with magenta at the half-way point.

It will be appreciated that if, instead of following the colours round the outer edges of the triangle, we pursue the same course parallel to these sides but at a distance nearer to the point W, we shall then get *pastel colours* or tints. Thus, if a line parallel to GREEN/RED is followed inside the triangle and nearer to W, we get those colours that result from mixtures of green and red, to which a certain amount of blue light has been added; and as the blue light

4

from the opposite corner begins to have some effect on the mixture, the result of the mingling of the three primary colours is to produce paler colours than are obtained along the outer edges of the triangle. The nearer the mixtures are taken to W in the centre of the triangle, the paler the colours become, until at the point W the resultant mixture is white. Thus, with the additive method of colour mixing,

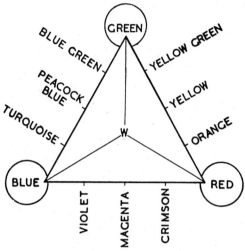

FIG. 2. MAXWELL COLOUR TRIANGLE, SHOWING THE COLOURS PRODUCED
FROM MIXTURES OF RED, GREEN, AND BLUE LIGHT

all colours corresponding to pure spectral hues and purple colours can be provided, together with the variety of tints that lie between these colours and white. (See also pages 9 and 135.)

THE SUBTRACTIVE METHOD OF MIXING COLOURS

From the foregoing, it will be seen that yellow is a secondary colour produced by mixtures of red and green light, and that green is a primary colour. Every artist knows, however, that the primary colours of pigments are red, yellow, and blue, and that green is produced by a mixture of yellow and blue paints. It should be explained here that the method of mixing paints and dyes is quite different from that of mixing coloured lights, and is known as the Subtractive Method. (See Plate I.) While the subtractive primary colours are generally named red, yellow, and blue, a more exact description would be magenta, yellow, and blue-green. When two pigments are mixing, physical action takes place and each colour destroys in the other those hues not common to both of them. Thus,

5

green is produced from the mixture of yellow and blue pigments, because the yellow reflects red and green light and the blue (which is really a blue-green) reflects green and blue light; so that, after inter-mixture, the only colour common to both of these primaries is the one that reflects green light, and therefore the mixture is said to be green.

When the primary colours of light—red, green, and blue—are superimposed, in proper proportions, the resultant phenomenon appears to be white; but when magenta, yellow, and peacock blue paints—i.e. the primary colours of paint—are mixed, the result is found to be black. It will be seen, therefore, that the Subtractive Method of mixing colours is the opposite of the Additive Method; and that, in fact, the primary colours of light correspond to the secondary colours of pigments, and vice versa. In each case, however, the onlooker is conscious of colour only because light rays corresponding to different colour hues enter directly or are reflected into his eye. With the Additive Method, one is dealing directly with the mixture of coloured light; whereas with the Subtractive Method, one is concerned with alterations in the colour of the reflected light.

REFLECTION, ABSORPTION, AND TRANSMISSION OF COLOUR

When light falls upon an object, one or more of three things must happen: the light rays are reflected, absorbed, or transmitted.

A plant may appear to have a red bloom and a green leaf because when light rays from the sun fall upon it, the bloom absorbs the green and blue rays and reflects only the red rays of light; while the leaf absorbs the red and blue rays and reflects only the green rays. The beholder, therefore, perceives an image of light corresponding to a red bloom and a green leaf. In addition to the reflection and absorption of light rays, the leaf, for example, might transmit certain light rays, and its appearance from the other side would be altered accordingly. If, instead of white light, a coloured light is thrown upon this plant, its appearance may be different because the light may not contain the colour that the plant reflects. Under peacock blue light the leaves of the plant would still appear green, but the bloom, instead of red, would probably appear a dark violet.

ACHROMATIC COLOURS, TINTS, AND SHADES

When considering colour from the standpoint of light, all colours are seen to be based upon the primaries, red, green, and blue, and thus all may be said to belong to the chromatic range. Artists and

6

designers, dealing with pigments, however, consider colours under two headings—

(*a*) Chromatic colours, such as red, yellow, green, blue.

(*b*) Achromatic colours, which are white, black, and intermediate greys.

In addition to pure colours, which match the spectral hues, there also are paler and darker colours, known as Tints, or pastel colours, and Shades, or neutral colours, and these are produced by mixing a chromatic with an achromatic colour. For example, pink could be produced by mixing magenta and white pigments, or a brown made by mixing red and dark grey pigments.

When mixing light, white light can be added to coloured light to make a pastel tint, or, as shown on the Maxwell Colour Triangle (Fig. 2), the same pastel colour can be matched by a suitable mixture of the three primary colours alone. It is not possible with light, however, to add in grey or black, as can be done with pigments, but the same result is achieved by reducing the lighting intensity of the colour relative to the general standard of illumination. In other words, we can make coloured light appear to be paler either by adding some white light or by suitably adjusting our three primary colours, thus making a pure colour into a tint, or pastel colour; and we can make it appear darker, or a neutral colour, by reducing its brightness relative to the brightness of other colours in the vicinity. This, perhaps, will be better understood when the factors Hue, Brightness, and Saturation are considered in the following paragraphs.

HUE, BRIGHTNESS, AND SATURATION

Any colour can be defined by the three factors: Hue, Brightness (Value or Brilliance), and Saturation (Chroma).

Hue is the attribute that leads us to describe colours as green, magenta, blue, etc. The principal hue of all colours (except the purples) may be represented by the spectral colours.

Brightness. This quality, often called " value " by the artist, and sometimes " brilliance," distinguishes a lighter from a darker colour by comparison with a surface of known brightness. Brightness can be diminished or increased without affecting the Hue or Saturation of a colour.

Saturation. With the subtractive method of colour mixing, this factor, sometimes called " chroma," is measured by the relative amount of white, grey, or black in a colour. A fully saturated colour is a pure colour and contains no such diluent, but when some white, grey, or black is added, then the colour becomes less

7

saturated. With the Additive Method of colour mixing, however, the term Saturation is employed to indicate the amount of white light in a colour. A fully saturated colour contains no element of white. When white light is present in the mixture, the colour is said to be less saturated.

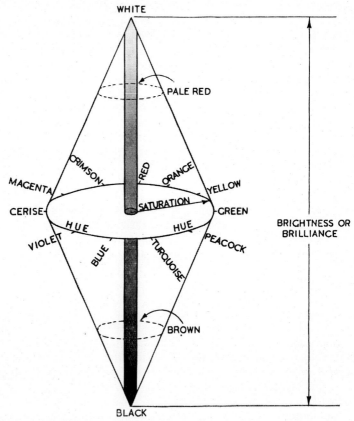

FIG. 3. DIAGRAM, SHOWING THE FACTORS OF HUE, BRIGHTNESS, AND SATURATION

By specifying the factors Hue, Brightness, and Saturation, it is possible to define any colour tint or shade. The Munsell System of Colour Notation, which has been adopted by the American Standards Association, classifies many hundreds of colours by specifying their hue, brightness (called value), and saturation (called chroma). The hues normally are divided into ten equal steps of colour discrimination, and each of these hues is qualified

8

by nine steps of value and many steps of chroma. It is possible, then, to specify say a *Mauve* as *Purple* 6/4, meaning the *Purple* hue at the 6th step of value, and the 4th step of chroma.

REACTION OF COLOURS ON EACH OTHER

The appearance of colours is not invariable, but is qualified by a number of factors that may be grouped under the heading of Environment. It is important that this fact be appreciated, because it makes the subject of colour somewhat complicated. These factors are specified by Dr. M. Luckiesh in his work *Colour and Its Applications* (Constable, London, and D. Van Nostrand, Co. Inc., New York), as—

(1) The intensity of the lighting.
(2) Spectral character of the light.
(3) Distribution of the light.
(4) The adaptation of the retina for light and colour.
(5) The duration of the stimulus, and the character of the stimulus preceding the one under consideration.
(6) The surroundings.
(7) The size and position of the retinal image.
(8) The surface character of the coloured medium.

It is not the purpose of this chapter to consider all aspects of colour in such detail, but it is important that we pay some attention to the *intensity of illumination, reflecting surfaces, spectral character of the light, after-images, and simultaneous contrast.*

These factors will be considered briefly in the following paragraphs, but first the relationship of complementary colours must be appreciated. If a surface receiving white light reflects the red rays and absorbs the green and blue rays, then the absorbed rays would make up a colour mixture that is said to be complementary to the colour of the light reflected. Again, complementary colours may be described as those that, when added together, produce white light. Thus, yellow and blue, green and magenta, red and peacock blue, are pairs of complementary colours. The Colour Triangle provides an easy method of ascertaining the complementary hue of any colour, for this can be found by taking a straight line from any point on a side of the triangle, through the point W to the opposite side line, the point of intersection on the latter indicating the complementary hue. Thus, a line from yellow through W will show that blue is the complementary hue of yellow. (See Fig. 2.)

Reverting to the factors that influence the appearance of a colour, it will be appreciated that the intensity of illumination plays an

9

important part; because, if the lighting intensity is increased, the colour of an object appears to be less saturated; and conversely, if the intensity is decreased, the colour appears to become more saturated. This factor is often closely related to the type of reflecting surface, because some surfaces tend to reflect a certain amount of light straight into the eye of the beholder, in addition to the colour rays that are selectively reflected, due to the colour of the object. Thus, a shiny red material, reflecting a certain amount of white light off the shiny surface in addition to the red rays diffusely reflected by the colour of the article, will appear to be paler in colour than is actually the case, and this effect will be more marked as the illumination intensity is increased. When coloured light falls upon a differently coloured object, there is always a change in the appearance of the latter, as has been briefly mentioned already. It is not proposed to deal further with this factor at this point, as the subject is more fully treated in Chapter 11.

AFTER-IMAGES

If we gaze for a short time at an electric lamp and then look away and close our eyes, we shall "see" a bright image that persists for a time and then fades away, until the image appears to be darker than the surroundings. The duration and strength of this after-image depends upon the brightness of the lamp and the time spent in looking at it. Again, if we gaze at a red lamp and then look away at a white surface, we shall "see" an after-image of the complementary colour: in other words, a blue-green image.

FIG. 4. SIMULTANEOUS CONTRAST

The grey centres in each of the six sections are exactly alike, but when seen against different backgrounds appear to vary considerably.

After-images occur as the natural outcome of gazing for even a short time at any bright or coloured object, though, of course, they are not as strong and persistent as those produced by looking at a very bright object such as an electric lamp. These after-images, however, are sufficient to play an important part in the appearance of colours, and are taken seriously into account by many artists.

If we gaze for a short time at a bright mauve object and then turn our eyes to a white surface, we shall "see" a pale green after-image where the mauve previously had stimulated the eye. After-images so seen are approximately complementary in hue to the colour that originally stimulated the eye, but generally these after-image colours are of a much paler hue. Thus, the after-image caused by gazing at a green object will tend to be pink, not magenta, in colour. This may account for temporary colour variations, though it is possible that these are due to the fact that the eye quickly tires when subjected to any colour, and therefore apparently becomes unduly sensitive to other colours, especially complementary colours. Whichever is the cause of the phenomenon, it is a fact that, if our eyes are moved, for example, from beholding a well-lighted red object on the stage to a blue object, the latter will appear at first to be more of a green-blue. Objects on a stage are often a bright colour and well illuminated, and every effort is made to hold the interest of the audience so that they continually gaze at these objects: temporary colour variation is therefore bound to play an important part in the colours seen by the audience, and due allowance should be made for it when we are choosing and grouping the stage colours. This is not difficult when it is realized that it is due to pale editions of colours complementary in hue to the dominant colours previously seen.

SIMULTANEOUS CONTRAST

The appearance of both chromatic and achromatic colours is greatly influenced by the mutual relationship of colours that are viewed simultaneously. Thus, in Fig. 4 it will be seen that although the grey centres in all cases are exactly equal in strength, they appear to vary considerably when viewed on these different backgrounds. Two or more colours viewed simultaneously in close proximity to each other also affect each other mutually, and, in some cases, the effect on their hues is very marked. When complementary colours are seen together, however, there is no change in hue, but each colour intensifies and sharpens the other. Contrasting colours, which are not complementary hues, tend to change their appearance when placed side by side. (See Plate II.)

Contrasting colours generally appear at their best when one colour greatly exceeds the other in area. If a small area of colour is superimposed on a larger area of a contrasting (but not complementary) hue, there is a tendency for the former to undergo a change equivalent to mixing with it a small amount of colour complementary in hue to the larger area. This will be appreciated when the phenomenon of after-images is considered, for it is seen that the eye tends to generate complementary colour images and to superimpose them on other areas, as though it is attempting always to create a balance: complementary colours added together constitute completeness.

CHAPTER 2

CONTROL AND MEASUREMENT OF ILLUMINATION

STAGE lighting has a scientific as well as an artistic basis. Knowledge of certain scientific facts concerning illumination is most useful and this chapter gives a brief résumé of those aspects of illuminating science and technique that are most likely to interest those engaged in the fascinating study of stage lighting.

REFLECTION AND REFRACTION

SPECULAR REFLECTION. When a surface is highly polished, like a mirror, it reflects, without scattering, a light beam falling upon it. The beam striking the surface, therefore, is reflected from it in the same form as before the reflection. Its direction is also

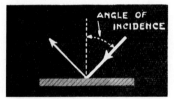

FIG. 5. SPECULAR REFLECTION

FIG. 6. SPREAD REFLECTION

fixed because the angle of reflection is always equal to the angle of incidence. (See Fig. 5.)

SPREAD REFLECTION. When a reflecting surface is not highly polished and smooth, it may reflect the light in a general direction as with specular reflection, though with a certain amount of diffusion due to a partial breaking-up of the beam; but the scattered rays have a definite general direction. In this case, the greatest intensity of the reflected beam occurs always at an angle which is equal to the angle of incidence. (See Fig. 6.)

DIFFUSE REFLECTION. When a beam of light falls upon a mat or rough surface, the light is reflected in a diffused manner, because the beam is broken up and the rays of light are scattered in all directions. For example, white blotting paper is a diffusing reflector. While the general direction of the reflected rays is independent of the incident angle of the light beam, the maximum intensity of the reflected light is always perpendicular to the reflecting surface. (See Fig. 7.)

The overall reflecting efficiency of a diffusing surface may be just as high as one that gives specular or spread reflection. In fact, white blotting paper has a very high reflection coefficient. With specular and spread reflection, however, the strength of the reflected light in certain directions is greater than in the case of diffuse reflection.

REFRACTION. Reflecting surfaces redirect the light beams falling upon them; but with transparent substances, such as glass, we are concerned with the phenomenon of refraction. A ray of light travels through the air in a straight line; but when it passes from air into a transparent medium, in general the direction of its path changes at the surface of separation. The light ray then continues through the transparent medium in a straight line; but when passing back into air, in general it again changes its direction at the surface of

FIG. 7. DIFFUSE REFLECTION | FIG. 8. REFRACTION

separation. (See Fig. 8.) Further examples of the redirection of light when passing through glass are shown in Figs. 9, 10, 11, and 12. This phenomenon, which is called refraction, does not take place when a light ray falls upon or leaves a piece of glass at right angles to its surface.

Any light ray meeting the surface at an angle other than at right angles to the surface is deflected from its straight course. The amount of refraction (as this deflection is called) becomes more pronounced as the angle between the incident ray and the surface of the glass diminishes. Similarly, when leaving glass to re-enter air, the light is again refracted, bending back to an angle more nearly parallel to the bounding surface of the glass. After refraction from air to glass, the path of the light ray is always more nearly perpendicular to the bounding surface than that of the incident ray, the amount of deviation varying with the angle of incidence according to a definite law.

When a light ray falls upon a flat piece of glass at an angle of 50° to the normal, about 7 per cent of the light is reflected and the remainder transmitted; but if this angle is increased, the amount of light reflected from the surface of the glass increases until at 85°

there is nearly total reflection. When a light ray travelling in glass or other transparent medium strikes the bounding surface, some of this light does not emerge but is reflected inside the glass, and the remainder is transmitted into air. The proportion of light reflected or transmitted varies according to this angle of incidence, but with

FIG. 9. TOTAL REFLECTING PRISM

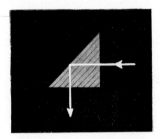

FIG. 10. REFRACTING PRISM

glass the proportion reflected begins to increase rapidly when the angle to the normal exceeds 35°, total internal reflection taking place at an angle of approximately 43°.

PRISMS. A piece of glass or transparent substance that is triangular in section is known as a prism. Prisms vary considerably in shape,

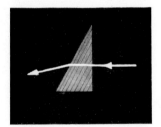

FIG. 11. REFRACTING PRISM

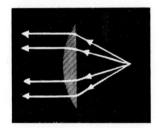

FIG. 12. REFRACTION OF LIGHT BY MEANS OF A LENS

as is shown in some examples in Figs. 9, 10, and 11; and it will be seen that in these cases the light ray direction is changed on leaving the glass. The type of prism shown in Fig. 9 causes the light ray to be reflected in the direction from which it came, and is known as a Total Reflecting Prism. The other examples are known as Refracting Prisms. Many types of scientific lighting glassware utilize prisms of different shapes in order to give the required control of light rays, and a familiar type on the stage is the prismatic lensplate (shown in Fig. 32) mounted in a spotlight.

15

LENSES. A lens may be constructed so that both surfaces are curved or one may be curved and the other plane. The flat side is known as plano, and the curved side as convex when it curves outwards and concave when it curves inwards. A plano-convex lens is therefore a lens with one curved and one flat side, and is a type frequently employed in stage spotlights. There are six main

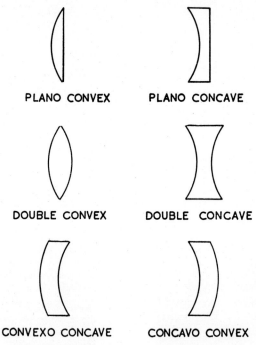

PLANO CONVEX   PLANO CONCAVE

DOUBLE CONVEX   DOUBLE CONCAVE

CONVEXO CONCAVE   CONCAVO CONVEX

FIG. 13. SIX TYPES OF LENSES IN GENERAL USE

classes of lenses and these are shown in Fig. 13. A convex lens is thickest at its axis, and when transmitting light rays refracts them towards this axis. A concave lens is thinnest at its axis and transmitted rays of light are refracted away from the axis.

FOCAL LENGTH

This is defined as the distance from the lens at which the image of an object at infinity (or a very long way away) is brought to a sharp focus. Expressed in another way, this means that the focal length is the distance of a point source of light from the optical centre of a lens that causes all the transmitted light rays to follow a path parallel with the axis of the lens. (See also Fig. 14.)

Optical systems provided in cinematograph projectors and certain forms of stage spotlights employ a combination of two or more lenses, but the standard stage spotlight normally employs only a single lens or lensplate.

MEASUREMENT OF LUMINOUS OUTPUT

The accepted unit for measurement of the luminous intensity of a light source is the International Candle, and the intensity of light is measured by *Candle Power* (c.p.). This cannot be taken as a direct measurement of the quantity of light emitted from the source,

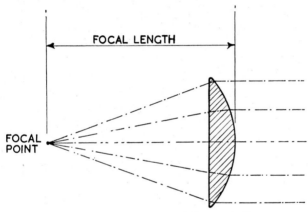

FIG. 14. FOCAL LENGTH OF A SPOTLIGHT LENS

as the candle power may vary in different directions. The *Mean Spherical Candle Power* (m.s.c.p.) is the average of candle power measured in all directions.

The luminous output of a light source is measured in *Lumens*. One lumen is the quantity of light that is received by a surface of 1 sq. ft., every elemental part of which is 1 ft. distant from a light source of one candle power. It can be shown that the total quantity of light emitted by a source equals $4\pi \times$ m.s.c.p. Hence, from a source of 1 m.s.c.p. a flux of 12·57 lumens is radiated.

MEASUREMENT OF ILLUMINATION

The unit of illumination is known as the *Foot Candle* (f.c.); and by definition, one foot candle is the illumination produced on a plane every elemental part of which is 1 ft. distant from a point

17

source of one candle power. It will be seen that the foot candle is related to the lumen in that the surface of 1 sq. ft. referred to above will have been illuminated to one foot candle. Thus, it will be seen that a flux of one lumen will be required to provide 1 sq. ft. of surface with an illumination of 1 f.c.

The illumination of a surface measured in foot candles indicates the amount of light falling on it and should not be confused with the brightness of the surface, which is a measure of the amount of light reflected by or emitted from the surface. It is possible for an article to look dull under good illumination because it reflects only a small portion of the incident light, or does not reflect the light into the eyes of the onlooker. This fact has an important bearing on stage lighting, as it is possible for a high intensity of illumination to fall upon an object that, while reflecting a large percentage of this light, does so in a direction away from the eyes of the audience, who, by receiving only a small percentage of the reflected light, are conscious only of a dullish object.

The brightness of a surface is often expressed in candles per square inch of projected area. Thus, a brightness of one candle per square inch indicates that each square inch of projected surface is emitting one candle power in the direction under consideration.

The *Foot Lambert* is another unit of brightness measurement, and in the case of a surface with a reflection factor of 80 per cent receiving an illumination of one foot candle and completely diffusing the light, the brightness of the surface is 0·8 Foot Lambert.

ILLUMINATION CALCULATIONS

The illumination intensity on a surface is inversely proportional to the square of the distance between the surface and the light source. Thus, the illumination produced on a surface 4 ft. from a lamp is four times greater than on a surface 8 ft. from the lamp; or, expressed in another way, a 100-watt lamp at a distance of 4 ft. from the surface gives the same illumination as four 100-watt lamps 8 ft. away. Expressed as an equation, this fundamental law of illumination (known as the Inverse Square Law) is—

Illumination (Foot Candles)

$$= \frac{\text{Candle Power of Light Source}}{\text{Square of the Distance in feet from Source to Surface}}$$

This equation is true, however, only if the surface is at right angles to the incident light rays; for when the rays strike the surface at an angle, the result obtained from the equation just given must be multiplied by the cosine of the angle of incidence of the light.

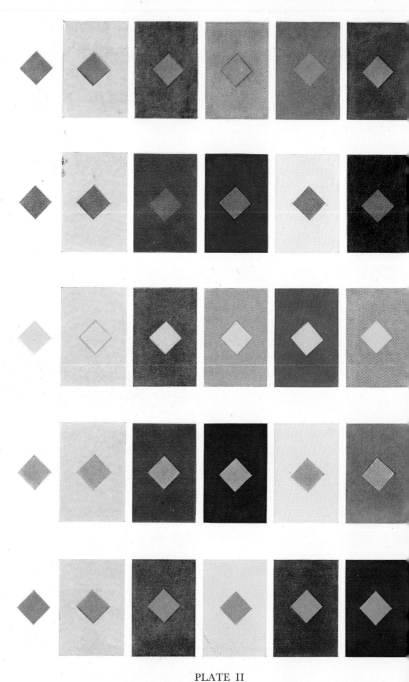

PLATE II
THE EFFECT OF COLOUR CONTRASTS
The colour value of the centre square is influenced by the colour of the background.

(G.290)

Table of Cosine Values for Angles 1° to 90°

ϕ^0	Cos ϕ	Cos³ ϕ	ϕ^0	Cos ϕ	Cos³ ϕ
0	1·000	1·000	45	0·707	0·354
1	1·000	1·000	46	0·695	0·335
2	0·999	0·998	47	0·682	0·317
3	0·999	0·996	48	0·669	0·300
4	0·998	0·993	49	0·656	0·282
5	0·996	0·989	50	0·643	0·266
6	0·995	0·984	51	0·629	0·249
7	0·993	0·978	52	0·616	0·233
8	0·990	0·971	53	0·602	0·218
9	0·988	0·964	54	0·588	0·203
10	0·985	0·955	55	0·574	0·189
11	0·982	0·946	56	0·559	0·175
12	0·978	0·936	57	0·545	0·162
13	0·974	0·925	58	0·530	0·149
14	0·970	0·913	59	0·515	0·137
15	0·966	0·901	60	0·500	0·125
16	0·961	0·888	61	0·485	0·114
17	0·956	0·875	62	0·470	0·103
18	0·951	0·860	63	0·454	0·0936
19	0·946	0·845	64	0·438	0·0842
20	0·940	0·830	65	0·423	0·0755
21	0·934	0·814	66	0·407	0·0673
22	0·927	0·797	67	0·391	0·0597
23	0·921	0·780	68	0·375	0·0526
24	0·914	0·762	69	0·358	0·0460
25	0·906	0·744	70	0·342	0·0400
26	0·899	0·726	71	0·326	0·0345
27	0·891	0·707	72	0·309	0·0295
28	0·883	0·688	73	0·292	0·0250
29	0·875	0·669	74	0·276	0·0209
30	0·866	0·650	75	0·259	0·0173
31	0·857	0·630	76	0·242	0·0142
32	0·848	0·610	77	0·225	0·0114
33	0·839	0·590	78	0·208	0·00899
34	0·829	0·570	79	0·191	0·00695
35	0·819	0·550	80	0·174	0·00524
36	0·809	0·530	81	0·156	0·00383
37	0·799	0·509	82	0·139	0·00270
38	0·788	0·489	83	0·122	0·00181
39	0·777	0·469	84	0·105	0·00114
40	0·766	0·450	85	0·0872	0·00066
41	0·755	0·430	86	0·0698	0·0003
42	0·743	0·410	87	0·0523	0·0001
43	0·731	0·391	88	0·0349	0·0000
44	0·719	0·372	89	0·0175	0·0000
45	0·707	0·354	90	0·0000	0·0000

Thus, if the light rays from a source of 100 candle power strike a surface 5 ft. away at an angle of 45°, the resultant illumination is—

Illumination (Foot Candles)

$$= \frac{100}{5^2} \times 0 \cdot 7 \text{ (i.e. cosine of angle of incidence).}$$

The resultant illumination is therefore 2·8 f.c.; whereas if the surface is at right angles to the light rays, the illumination is 4 f.c. It is much more convenient in many calculations to deal with the distance of the light source from the surface at right angles to the latter, because this removes the necessity to calculate the slant distance between the light source and the point of incidence, and the resultant illumination can then be found as follows—

$$\text{Illumination (Foot Candles)} = \frac{\text{Candle Power}}{H^2} \times \cos^3 \phi.$$

The Candle Power is that of the light source in the direction of the point of incidence on the surface; H is the height of the source above the plane of the surface; and $\cos^3 \phi$ is the cube of the cosine of the angle of incidence of the light at the point concerned. In calculating the illumination at various points on a flat surface from a given light source, the factor H is constant, and it is necessary to determine only the angles for the various points and the candle power of the source at those angles to calculate the answer quickly. It is necessary, of course, to have a table of cosine values for the angles, and this is given on page 19.

SPOTLIGHTS AND THE INVERSE SQUARE LAW

While the Inverse Square Law is easy to understand and apply, when dealing with spotlights or projectors giving a narrow angle beam of light it is important to realize that the distance from the light source to the illuminated surface is calculated, in this case, not from the actual light source, but from a theoretical point in space where the straight sides of the line beam would merge, if followed back far enough for this to take place. Thus, a spotlight with an 8 in. diameter lens, giving a light beam with a total beam width of 10°, would have a theoretical focal point approximately 3 ft. 9 in. back from the lens. To apply the Inverse Square Law, this distance should be added to the actual distance between the spotlight lens and the illuminated surface. Thus, if this spotlight gives 10 f.c. when 10 ft. away from the illuminated surface, it is assumed for practical purposes that its candle power at the focal point in space is 1890, and not 1000 as might at first appear.

REFLECTOR AND LENS EFFICIENCY

By redirecting light rays, a reflector can increase the strength of light in a given direction, but no reflector can provide a quantity of light greater than that which falls upon it. No reflector has 100 per cent efficiency, so in practice the total quantity of reflected light is always less than the quantity incident upon it.

The amount of light flux that can be redirected by a reflector is therefore dependent upon the actual reflector efficiency and the light flux falling upon it. Thus, if a reflector that is 90 per cent

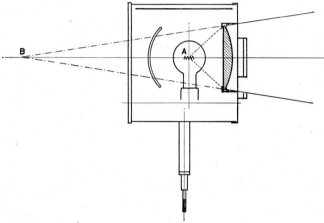

Fig. 15. Inverse Square Law: Assumed Focal Point for a Spotlight Lens

The focal point for the spotlight lens is shown in (*A*), but when applying the Inverse Square Law for illumination calculations, the focal length must be assumed to extend to (*B*).

efficient is required to throw a narrow, concentrated beam of light from a lamp giving 1000 lumens, it redirects only 90 lumens if its size is such that only 10 per cent of the luminous output from the lamp falls upon it; whereas if it is designed to collect 50 per cent of the luminous flux, it then redirects 450 lumens in the required direction.

This zone factor is very important and should often be taken more into account than actual reflector efficiency, because there is not a great deal of difference between the efficiency of many popular forms of reflecting surfaces, whereas the difference in zone factor between reflectors of different sizes may be most marked.

The zone factor applies also to lenses, because here again the total amount of light transmitted by a lens depends upon the lens efficiency as well as on the quantity of light incident upon it. Some spotlights, for example, have a poor zone factor and control less than 15 per cent of the luminous output of the lamp. The distance of a lens from the light source is therefore important, because an 8 in. diameter lens at 10 in. controls approximately the same amount of light as a 6 in. lens at $7\frac{3}{4}$ in. from the light source.

PART II. THE ADAPTATION AND CONTROL OF LIGHT

∎

CHAPTER 3

LIGHT SOURCES AND COLOUR FILTERS

IN Chapter 1 we have seen that white light is really a combination of certain hues of coloured light, and daylight, for example, is made up of all the colour hues seen in the visible spectrum. Illuminating engineering generally deals with light as white light, and most of the terms and definitions in common use appertain to white light. This is a convenient procedure because coloured light, in practice, is usually obtained by passing white light through a colour filter that subtracts from white light those colours not required in the final hue.

COLOUR FILTERS

The filter may be a gelatine or glass screen, a coloured envelope (for example, the bulb) round the lamp filament, or some other convenient form. Whatever it is, its function is the same: namely, to subtract from the light given out by the light source certain colour hues that are complementary to the colour actually required. Working on the basis of red, green, and blue as primary colours, we require a filter that absorbs blue light and transmits red and green light in order to obtain yellow. To obtain magenta light, we require a filter that transmits red and blue light, but absorbs the complementary colour, i.e. green. If we require, say, pale pink light, we must have a filter that transmits red and blue light but only partially transmits green. This can be readily appreciated from Maxwell's Triangle shown in Fig. 2.

No colour filter can create coloured light; it can absorb certain hues only and transmit others; if the required hues are not present in the original light, then the filter cannot transmit them. Thus, a colour filter intended to give red light will transmit practically no light at all if placed in front of a mercury vapour discharge lamp, because the latter generates only green-blue light, which this filter will not transmit, and there is only a trace of red light emanating from the light source to pass through the filter. When dealing with colour filters, it is important, therefore, to consider the spectral character of the illuminant; and this will be borne in mind in the

23

discussion, in this chapter, of the various light sources available for use in stage lighting equipment.

Besides the spectral character and lumen output of an illuminant, there are the factors of running cost, size and shape of filament, heat, working life, and lamp dimensions to be borne in mind when considering a light source. These factors vary considerably according to the type of illuminant, and as there is a large number of light sources available for use on an electricity supply, only those in general use will be considered.

TUNGSTEN FILAMENT VACUUM LAMPS

Standard vacuum lamps are available to-day in two sizes only, 15 watts and 25 watts, as larger sizes have been replaced by the gas-filled lamp, which has a higher efficiency. The latter is not very suitable for dipping in coloured lacquer, as the glass bulb gets rather too hot; vacuum lamps are sometimes still used for this purpose, although their low wattage range considerably restricts their use.

Strip light vacuum lamps in sizes 30 watts and 60 watts are available and can be supplied in standard colours: red, orange, yellow, green, blue, flame, pink, and white. The lamps are provided with centre contact type caps at both ends. Opal tubular lamps can be supplied in standard colours: blue, green, yellow, amber, orange, flame, pink, red, and white.

GENERAL SERVICE GAS-FILLED LAMPS

Gas-filled lamps with clear glass bulbs are available in sizes ranging from 40 watts to 1500 watts. Pearl gas-filled lamps, which are similar to the clear lamps except that the bulbs are frosted inside, are available in sizes ranging from 40 watts to 150 watts. The *clear* gas-filled lamp is the much more suitable for use in stage lighting equipment fitted with concentrating type reflectors, owing to the sharper focus that the filament will provide. Unless the reflector is a large one, it is difficult to get the proper focal results from a pearl lamp, and in small lighting units, as, for example, a compartment in a magazine type footlight, there is actual light obstruction from the pearl bulb. The diffusing nature of a pearl bulb tends to soften shadows to a certain extent.

General service clear and pearl gas-filled lamps are made with coiled coil filament as standard, in sizes ranging between 40 watts and 100 watts—the advantage being an increase of up to 20 per cent in the lumen output per watt compared with the single coil type of filament, which is used, however, in the other lamp sizes.

Lamps up to 100 watts in size are provided with bayonet type (B.C.) caps. The 150-watt size can be supplied with either a bayonet or an Edison screw (E.S.) type cap. The 200-watt lamp is provided with an Edison screw cap and all larger sizes with a Goliath Edison screw (G.E.S.) cap. Many theatre engineers prefer to have Edison screw caps on *all* lamp bulbs up to 200 watts in size, as this obviates the possibility of a lamp's jumping out of the holder owing to faulty fitment. Edison screw holders can be supplied to special order on lamps of 100 watts and less in size.

The lumen output per watt increases with the size of the lamp, and is greater with 100–130-volt lamps than with 200–260-volt lamps.

This is shown in the following table—

VOLTAGE RANGE	STANDARD WATTS	STANDARD CAP	LENGTH MM.	TOL. ±	DIAMETER MM. TOL.	LIGHT CENTRE LENGTH MM.	AVERAGE LUMENS THROUGHOUT LIFE	
							SINGLE COIL	COILED COIL
100–130 200–260	15	B.C. B.C.	92·5	3·5	55 ± 1	65 ± 3	133 113	
100–130 200–260	25	B.C. B.C.	100	3·5	60 ± 1	70 ± 3	228 206	
100–130 200–260	40	B.C. B.C.	110	3·5	60 ± 1	80 ± 3	449 330	389
100–130 200–260	60	B.C. B.C.	117·5	3·5	65 ± 1	85 ± 3	759 584	665
100–130 200–260	75	B.C. B.C.	125	3·5	70 ± 1	90 ± 3	1000 785	883
100–130 200–260	100	B.C. B.C.	137·5	3·5	75 ± 1	100 ± 3	1400 1160	1270
100–130 200–260	150	B.C. E.S.	160	4·5	80 ± 1	120 ± 4	2230 1970	
100–130 200–260	200	E.S. E.S.	178	5·5	90 ± 1	133 ± 5	3090 2725	
100–130 200–260	300	G.E.S. G.E.S.	233	7	110 ± 1·5	178 ± 6	4950 4430	
100–130 200–260	500	G.E.S. G.E.S.	267	8	130 ± 1·5	202 ± 7	8950 7930	
100–130 200–260	750	G.E.S. G.E.S.	300	9	150 ± 1·5	225 ± 8	14270 12740	
100–130 200–260	1000	G.E.S. G.E.S.	300	9	150 ± 1·5	225 ± 8	19640 17800	
100–130 200–260	1500	G.E.S. G.E.S.	335	9	170 ± 1·5	250 ± 8	30220 28380	

Note. Coiled coil lamps in these wattages are not necessarily available.

The increased efficiency of the larger lamps is an interesting point to bear in mind. For example, on a 200-volt supply the average luminous output of a 150-watt lamp is 1970 lumens, and that of a 1500-watt lamp is 28,380 lumens. Thus, while the current consumption of ten 150-watt lamps would be the same as for one 1500-watt lamp, the latter would give nearly 50 per cent more light.

The filament construction of gas-filled lamps takes the form of a ring type filament for sizes up to 300 watts, but for the larger sizes is of the zigzag type. These filament constructions are not suitable for use in spotlights and other apparatus requiring a concentrated type of light source.

Colour sprayed gas-filled lamps can be supplied in sizes ranging between 40 watts and 750 watts. The bulbs are coated with a layer of unglazed china, which gives a very highly diffused light, and in normal times they are available in standard colours: white, red, pink, orange, yellow, green, blue, and flame tint. The manufacturers do not guarantee uniformity of colour, and the red, green, and blue colours are not very suitable for use as primaries for three-colour mixing. Gas-filled lamps with the bulbs made of coloured glass also are available. They are made in three sizes, 40 watts, 60 watts, and 100 watts, and the colours are green, blue, amber, and ruby.

GAS-FILLED PROJECTOR LAMPS

The filament construction of a standard gas-filled lamp is not suitable for use in stage spotlights and optical effects equipment, and in the larger sizes the physical dimensions of the lamp bulb are in themselves rather too large to be conveniently accommodated. Gas-filled projector lamps, therefore, are available for use in this kind of apparatus, and the bulb dimensions and filament construction are suitably designed for this particular purpose. To suit the different needs of various kinds of equipment there are many different types of projector lamps, varying in size, shape, filament, construction, and luminous efficiency.

In the past there have been nine classes of projector lamps in common use, and all but one were employed to some extent in modern stage lighting. Lately there has been considerable rationalization of types, and Classes A2 and A3 lamps are likely to become obsolete. The outstanding features of the remaining types suitable for use in stage equipment are given below.

CLASS AI

This is a tubular shaped bulb and is for burning in a vertical position with the cap downwards. The luminous efficiency is high, and the filament is of the grid type making it suitable for use in optical lanterns and projectors as well as in spotlights. When burned in the normal vertical position, its approximate life is 50 hours, but if the bulb is tilted this life will be reduced, and if the tilt exceeds 10 per cent the bulb may burn out very quickly.

The narrow diameter of the lamp enables a lens or reflector to be brought fairly close to the actual filament, giving control of a greater quantity of light flux than is possible with the round type lamps.

The range of lamps available in this class and their light output is shown in the following table—

VOLTAGE	WATTS	STANDARD CAP	DIAM. MM.	OVERALL LENGTH	LIGHT CENTRE LENGTH	LIFE HOURS
12	100	P.28/25	25 ± 1	133 ± 7	55·5 ± 0·5	50
30	100	P.28/25	25 ± 1	133 ± 7	55·5 ± 0·5	50
	900	P.40/41	64 ± 2	235 ± 10	84 ± 0·5	50
50	25	B.15S/21	16 ± 1	57 ± 3	29 ± 2	50
	250	P.28/25	32 ± 2	133 ± 7	55·5 ± 0·5	50
115	300	P.28/25	32 ± 2	133 ± 7	55·5 ± 0·5	25
	500	P.28/25	32 ± 2	133 ± 7	55·5 ± 0·5	25
	750	P.28/25	38 ± 2	133 ± 7	55·5 ± 0·5	25
	50	B.15S	25 ± 1	76 ± 3	34·5 ± 2	50
	100	P.28/25	25 ± 1	133 ± 7	55·5 ± 2	50
	250	P.28/25	32 ± 2	133 ± 7	55·5 ± 0·5	50
	500	P.28/25	64 ± 2	133 ± 7	55·5 ± 0·5	50
	1000	P.40/41	64 ± 2	235 ± 10	84 ± 0·5	50
200–250	100	P.28/25	25 ± 1	133 ± 7	55·5 ± 0·5	50
	250	P.28/25	32 ± 2	133 ± 7	55·5 ± 0·5	50
	500	P.28/25	64 ± 2	133 ± 7	55·5 ± 0·5	50
	1000	P.40/41	64 ± 2	235 ± 10	84 ± 0·5	50

CLASS B I

This is probably the most popular lamp for stage work, because it is small and compact, and can be used in any position except within 45° of the vertical with the cap upwards. Few, if any, stage spotlights are designed for the lamp to burn in the forbidden position, and this means that in most cases the spotlights can be tilted at any reasonable angle without damage to the lamp. The filament construction is not so compact as in the A1 Class; the luminous efficiency is lower, but this is compensated by the longer

FIG. 16. TYPICAL STAGE SPOTLIGHT FOR USE WITH 1000-WATT CLASS B1 PROJECTOR LAMP
(*Reproduced by Courtesy of W. J. Furse & Co., Ltd.*)

life, which is approximately 800 hours. Class B1 Bulbs are particularly suitable for overhead spotlights and are available in the following ranges—

VOLTAGE	WATTS	STANDARD CAP	DIAM. MM.	OVERALL LENGTH	LIGHT CENTRE LENGTH	LIFE HOURS
115	100	E.27/25	80 ± 2	115 ± 10	75 ± 5	800
	250	E.27/25	95 ± 2	125 ± 10	75 ± 5	800
	500	E.40/45	130 ± 5	180 ± 10	115 ± 5	800
	1000	E.40/45	130 ± 5	180 ± 10	115 ± 5	800
200–250	100	E.27/25	80 ± 2	115 ± 10	75 ± 5	800
	250	E.27/25	95 ± 2	125 ± 10	75 ± 5	800
	500	E.40/45	130 ± 5	180 ± 10	115 ± 5	800
	1000	E.40/45	130 ± 5	180 ± 10	115 ± 5	800

CLASS B2

This lamp is similar to the B1 Class, except that its overall length is much greater. However, it can be burnt in any position, including cap upwards. It is available in two sizes only: 500 watts and 1000 watts.

CLASS E

This is a compact, round bulb lamp, especially designed for use in Epidiascope apparatus, but it can be used also in spotlights where the lamp is burnt cap downwards within 45° either side of the vertical. It is available in the 500-watt size only, as follows—

VOLTAGE	WATTS	STANDARD CAP	DIAM. MM.	OVERALL LENGTH	LIGHT CENTRE LENGTH	LIFE HOURS
115	500	P.28/25	100 ± 2	135 ± 10	60 ± 0·5	100
200–250	500	P.28/25	100 ± 2	135 ± 10	60 ± 0·5	100

CLASS F

This type of lamp is for use on voltages ranging from 6 volts to 18 volts, and it gives a very intense, concentrated light owing to the small area of the filament. The lamps have a high luminous efficiency and most sizes have a burning life of approximately 100 hours. The range of lamps available is as follows—

VOLTAGE	WATTS	STANDARD CAP	DIAM. MM.	OVERALL LENGTH	LIGHT CENTRE LENGTH	LIFE HOURS
6	30	E.14/23 × 15	35 ± 2	57 ± 5	47 ± 5	25*
6	48	B.15/25 × 18	35 ± 2	65 max.	40 ± 3	100*
12	24	B.15/25 × 18	38 ± 2	60 ± 5	44 ± 5	100*
12	48	E.14/23 × 15	50 ± 2	70 ± 5	40 ± 3	100†
18	9	E.10/20 × 13	18 ± 1	36 ± 3	25 ± 2	100‡

* These are transverse filament.   † Twin pillar filament.   ‡ Round bulb.

CINEMA STUDIO LAMPS

These are available in two types.

(a) Round bulb type in 5000-watt size.

(b) Bi-post lamps in 2000-watt and 5000-watt sizes.

The round bulb lamp can be burnt at any reasonable angle and is specially suitable for use in cinema studio equipment, but sometimes it is employed in large stage spotlights. The luminous efficiency is high and the life is approximately 100 hours. The bi-post lamps are provided with a special two-pin cap, as the name indicates. Apart from the positive nature of the electrical contact, this ensures that the filament is accurately located in position when inserted in the lamp holder. The range of bi-post lamps available is as follows—

VOLTAGE	WATTS	STANDARD CAP	DIAM. MM.	OVERALL LENGTH	LIGHT CENTRE LENGTH	LIFE HOURS
115	2000	Bi-post	152·5 ± 2	232 ± 6	127 ± 2	100
	5000	Bi-post	203 ± 2	335 ± 6	165 ± 2	100
240	2000	Bi-post	152·5 ± 2	232 ± 6	127 ± 2	100
	5000	Bi-post	203 ± 2	335 ± 6	165 ± 2	100

REFLECTOR LAMPS

These lamps are parabolic in shape and have the upper part coated on the inside with aluminium to form a highly efficient

internal reflector which enables the light output to be used with maximum effectiveness. This reflector is protected as well as constructed by the glass of the lamp bulb and does not tarnish. Therefore its initial efficiency is maintained throughout the life of the lamp. These lamps are available in the "spotlight" type with either Ring- or Grid-type filaments and can also be obtained with "flood" type distribution. They are complete pieces of lighting apparatus to which colour filters can be attached.

Fig. 16a. 150-Watt Reflector Spot-light Lamp with Internal Parabolic Mirror Finish
(*Reproduced by Courtesy of E.L.M.A. Lighting Service Bureau*)

The lamp should be especially useful to small theatres with limited budgets.

ELECTRIC DISCHARGE AND FLUORESCENT LAMPS

In recent years, the electric discharge lamp has replaced the gas-filled lamp to a considerable extent for certain industrial and commercial uses. The luminous efficiency is approximately $2\frac{1}{2}$ times greater, and certain types of discharge lamp (e.g. the fluorescent tube) can give a light more closely resembling daylight. The two main types of electric discharge lamps are (a) the mercury type and (b) the sodium type.

The former provides a light that is fundamentally green-blue, whereas the sodium type gives a bright yellow light. The monochromatic nature of the illumination, except of fluorescent mercury lamps, renders them of little value for stage work, although plain mercury discharge lamps have been used effectively for the floodlighting of cyclorama backgrounds. Electric discharge lamps cannot yet be dimmed out fully in the same manner as gas-filled lamps are. As the ability to dim out fully is an important factor in stage lighting, electric discharge lamps are not likely to play a very big part until some suitable means of doing this is found.

A recent development is the fluorescent mercury discharge lamp, which is available in both bulb and tube form, and the latter has had an almost revolutionary effect on certain fields of industrial and commercial lighting. In each type the inside of the glass bulb is covered with a specially prepared fluorescent powder that is stimulated by the ultra-violet radiation from the mercury discharge. The light from the discharge itself blends with the light from the fluorescent powder. As the powder can be made to glow in colour, the final effect can be made to approximate to white light or any desired tint. This means that the outside of the bulb or glass tube for all practical purposes becomes a light source. Thus, owing to the large area of the light source, fluorescent lamps are not so suitable for use in lighting equipment designed for accurate control of the emitted light. While fluorescent tubular lamps could be employed, say, for floodlighting on the stage, they are not so suitable for use in equipment designed to give narrow, concentrated beams of light.

The bluish-green light provided by the ordinary mercury type discharge lamp, and the yellowish light given by the sodium type give a very unnatural appearance to coloured objects. While unsuitable for ordinary stage illumination, these lamps may be useful for certain trick effects. The spectrum of light is not continuous and the light emission is concentrated into very narrow bands of the spectrum. This means that both mercury and sodium type discharge lamps cannot be used in conjunction with gelatine or other stage colour filters. The fluorescent tube mercury discharge lamp, however, provides a reasonably continuous spectrum and can be used with ordinary colour filters. The general colour rendering of articles seen under fluorescent tube white lighting is good.

HIGH PRESSURE MERCURY VAPOUR LAMPS

A small high pressure type of mercury vapour lamp with a small concentrated light source and light emission covering all the visible spectrum is now available. The lamp consists of a quartz bulb containing two tungsten electrodes between which an arc of high brightness burns steadily. Owing to its small, concentrated source, the lamp is suitable for use in spotlights and projectors, though the light has a bluish-green tint that affects the colour of the light given through gelatine and other colour filters. Occasions arise when the high efficiency of the lamp is more important than the correct colour rendering, as, for example, in the case of film projectors for monochromatic film. The lamp wattage is 250 and is intended for operation on A.C. mains of 200–250 volts; a special choke must be used in series with it. The lamp can be operated on D.C. mains also, but a special device to strike the arc may be necessary.

Water-cooled types of high pressure mercury vapour lamps also are available, but at present they are of little value for stage work, although they have important advantages for photographic purposes.

BLACK GLASS ULTRA-VIOLET LAMPS AND U.V. FILTERS

Fluorescent powders and dyes, when excited by ultra-violet light, glow in white or colour according to their composition. This phenomenon can be used effectively on the stage, and the necessary ultra-violet light can be obtained either by " black glass " lamp bulbs or by ultra-violet filters placed in front of carbon arc spotlights or mercury vapour lamps.

Ultra-violet light is invisible; a stage lighted by these rays appears to be in darkness and only objects treated with fluorescent powders or dyes can be seen.

The normal paints and dyes available for this purpose fluoresce only when they are under the ultra-violet light and have no phosphorescent effect, so that when the light is switched off the fluorescent effect vanishes.

The black glass bulb comprises a 125-watt lamp with the bulb itself providing the ultra-violet filter. In common with most discharge lamps, this black glass bulb lamp must be used on an A.C. supply in conjunction with a suitable choke and condenser. The lamp is available for use on standard voltages between 200 and 250 volts.

Special ultra-violet flat glass filters can be obtained, and if these are used in conjunction with carbon arc spotlights they give very good results. These ultra-violet glass filters can be employed also with mercury vapour lamps.

CARBON ARC LAMPS

Another type of light source is the carbon arc, which provides a small and intense source in the form of an arc. When two carbon rods, through which an electric current is flowing, are made to touch and are then separated, they strike an arc, which causes the carbons to burn off at a very high temperature. It is necessary to feed the carbons together as they burn away, in order to maintain the width of the gap; and in most stage arc projectors this is accomplished by hand-operated mechanism, though in cinematograph projectors the feed is electrically automatic.

The small, concentrated area of the light source is particularly suitable for use with lens systems, and enables the light to be controlled accurately. Together with the amount of light emitted, this causes a beam of sufficient intensity for longer throws, as, for example, from the rear of the auditorium to the stage. A more efficient form of arc mechanism than the ordinary carbon arc is the high intensity type, which utilizes special cored carbons, electrically rotated or provided with other means to ensure that they burn evenly. This enables a small diameter crater of uniform shape and size to be maintained on the positive carbon and allows the use of very efficient optical systems.

Until recently, carbon arcs could be effectively operated only from a D.C. supply, but carbons have now been produced that enable satisfactory results to be obtained from an A.C. supply. D.C. arc spotlights require a thicker carbon for the positive electrode because this burns away more quickly than the negative, but with the A.C. arc both can be of the same diameter.

SPECTRAL COMPOSITION OF ELECTRIC LIGHT

Tungsten filament lamps (both vacuum and gas-filled types) provide a spectrum of light very different from that given out by the sun. The proportion of red and yellow rays is greater and there is a considerable deficiency in the rays at the blue end of the spectrum. This emphasis on the red end of the spectrum causes the light to appear yellowish in hue compared to daylight, and emphasizes the red and yellow factors in colours, while bluish colours appear to be darkened appreciably in hue.

The spectral composition of the light varies with the size of the lamp, the emphasis on the red end of the spectrum being more

33

marked with the smaller lamps. The larger-sized gas-filled lamps give a whiter light as there is a smaller deficiency at the blue end of the spectrum. Furthermore, most projector type gas-filled lamps run at a higher filament temperature, and give an even whiter light than standard gas-filled lamps. This is because the higher filament temperature provides a bluer light, while at lower temperatures the light is redder in hue.

By " overrunning " or " underrunning " a gas-filled lamp, the spectral composition of the light is altered, because the temperature of the lamp filament is affected. Variations in voltage also have a very marked effect on the actual light output and it is important that this fact should be appreciated, because the variation in light output and quality changes very sharply with the voltage, as can be seen from the curves shown in Fig. 17. For example, a lamp rated at 100 watts on a 230-volt supply gives approximately 68 per cent of its normal light output when operated on a 210-volt supply, while the spectral composition of the light is changed and there is a marked decrease of light emission at the blue end of the spectrum; this causes the light to become more yellowish in hue and give poorer colour rendering.

Alternatively, a 210-volt lamp operated on a 230-volt supply gives approximately 38 per cent more light, with a marked increase at the blue end of the spectrum, causing a much whiter light with better powers of colour rendering.

The life of a gas-filled lamp is affected also if the filament burns at a higher or lower temperature, and " overrunning " a lamp shortens its life, while " underrunning " lengthens it. Thus, in the examples just considered, the life is reduced by three-quarters when the lamp is " overrun " by 9 per cent and increased several times when " underrun " by 9 per cent. Gas-filled projector lamps are rated with a shorter life than standard gas-filled lamps, and certain types give a higher luminous output per watt than ordinary lamps.

In view of the small percentage of light at the blue end of the spectrum given by the gas-filled lamp, it is sometimes considered wise slightly to " overrun " lamp bulbs used behind blue colour filters, as there is then a marked increase in light that more than compensates for the shortened life of the lamp.

It will be seen from the curves in Fig. 17 that the reduction of light output is more rapid than the reduction of the wattage, and therefore it is rarely economical to run lamps at less than their rated voltage. In fact, for stage work it is often more economical to " overrun " lamps slightly, because the cost of replacement of bulbs may represent only a small part of the cost of providing the necessary illumination.

THEATRE GELATINES AND FILTERS

Colour filters made of gelatine are available in a range of about forty colours in Great Britain, and are generally known by the names and reference numbers shown below. These gelatine names

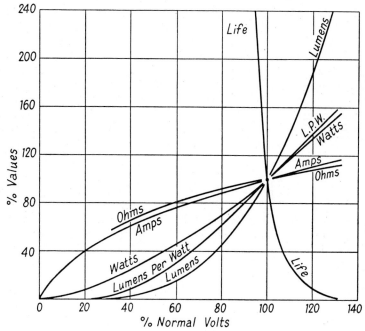

FIG. 17. GRAPH SHOWING THE EFFECT OF VOLTAGE VARIATION
ON LIGHT OUTPUT OF GAS-FILLED LAMPS

From Theory and Design of Illuminating Engineering Equipment (*Jolley, Waldram & Wilson*) *by Courtesy of Chapman & Hall, Ltd.*)

and numbers are not standard with all manufacturers in Great Britain but are the ones most used in the professional theatre. The material is supplied in sheets which usually measure 22 in. × 17½ in., and have a thickness of 0·005 in.

No. 1. Clear Yellow	No. 6. Clear Red
2. Clear Amber	7. Clear Light Rose
3. Clear Straw	8. Clear Salmon
4. Clear Medium Amber	9. Clear Middle Salmon
5. Clear Orange	10. Clear Middle Rose
5a. Deep Orange	11. Clear Dark Pink

No. 12. Clear Deep Rose
13. Clear Magenta
14. Clear Ruby
15. Clear Peacock Blue
16. Clear Moonlight Blue
17. Clear Steel Blue
18. Clear Middle Blue
19. Clear Dark Blue
20. Clear Deep Blue
21. Clear Pea Green
22. Clear Moss Green
23. Clear Light Green
24. Clear Dark Green
25. Clear Purple
26. Clear Mauve

No. 29. Heavy Frost
31. Light Frost
32. Clear Medium Blue
33. Clear Deep Amber
36. Clear Lavender
39. Clear Green
40. Light Blue
50. Clear Pale Yellow
51. Clear Gold Tint
52. Clear Pale Gold
53. Clear Pale Salmon
54. Clear Pale Rose
55. Clear Chocolate Tint
56. Clear Pale Chocolate
60. Clear Pale Grey

Sheets of colour media can be obtained also in other materials, belonging to the cellulose acetate group. Usually these are supplied in larger sheets than gelatines, for example, 49 in. × 21 in., while the thickness is often greater, i.e. 0·010 in. or 0·020 in. The manufacturers frequently claim a greater mechanical strength and durability for these filters compared with gelatine sheets, but often they are not available in the same range of colours as theatre gelatines, and in the past it has been difficult to match the very pale tints. It is important that colour filters should be made of non-inflammable material; some licensing authorities are very strict on this point.

Coloured glass is also available, but the range of colour hues is limited, and colours are apt to vary with different pieces of glass. It tends to absorb more light than gelatine and similar filters, and is of course breakable.

The American range of theatre gelatines is larger than the British range and comprises over seventy colours. Century Lighting, Inc., of New York City, for example, list their range of gelatines as follows.

No. 0. Clear
1. Frost
2. Light Flesh Pink
3. Flesh Pink
4. Medium Pink
5. Pink
6. Rose Pink
7. Dark Rose Pink
8. Deep Pink
9. du Barry Pink
10. Light Magenta
11. Medium Magenta
12. Dark Magenta
13. Rose
14. Rose Purple
15. Dark Rose Purple
16. Violet
17. Special Lavender

18. Medium Lavender
19. Dark Lavender
20. Light Purple
21. Purple
22. Royal Purple
23. Medium Purple
24. Dark Purple
25. Daylight Blue
26. Light Sky Blue
27. Light Blue
28. Light Navy Blue
29. Special Steel Blue
30. Light Blue Special
31. Medium Sky Blue
32. Medium Blue Special
33. Medium Blue
34. Medium Navy Blue
35. Dark Sky Blue

No. 36. Non-fade Blue
    37. Dark Blue
    38. Dark Navy Blue
    39. Urban Blue
    40. Light Green Blue
    41. Moonlight Blue
    42. Nile Blue
    43. Light Blue Green
    44. Medium Blue Green
    45. Blue Green
    46. Dark Blue Green
    47. Light Green
    48. Medium Green
    49. Dark Green
    50. Light Lemon
    51. Medium Lemon
    52. Dark Lemon
    53. Very Light Straw
    54. Light Straw
    55. Medium Straw

No. 56. Dark Straw
    57. Light Amber
    58. Medium Amber
    59. Amber
    60. Dark Amber
    61. Orange
    62. Light Scarlet
    63. Special Light Red
    64. Light Red
    65. Medium Scarlet
    66. Pink Red
    67. Fire Red
    68. Pure Red
    69. Pure Chocolate
    70. Chocolate
    75. Grey
    80. Variegated
    90. Variegated
    95. Variegated
  100. Rainbow

Gelatines used in the United States and Canada are usually thinner than those used in Great Britain, but they are amazingly strong and durable in spite of their thinness.

A deeper colour can be obtained by using two thicknesses of gelatine together. Some manufacturers offer colour filter material in two or more thicknesses. A thicker material will give a deeper colour, and will probably last much longer.

The exact colour of the light obtained from any colour filter depends to a certain extent upon the nature of the light source. It will be found, for example, that pinkish filters give quite different results when used in front of, say, 1000-watt and then 100-watt gas-filled lamps, or in front of a carbon arc. The colour variation is most marked in the case of colour filters transmitting a certain amount of blue light. In the case of yellow filters, the difference may be hardly noticeable.

The same remarks apply to overrunning or underrunning a lamp: there is a marked increase in the proportion of blue light when a lamp is overrun, and a deficiency when it is underrun.

In the same way, certain colours of light obtained through filters change appreciably in hue when the lamps are dimmed. In some colours, most noticeably the pinks, this change is very apparent. No. 36 Lavender gelatine, for example, gives a very different colour when the lamp is partly dimmed.

Practically all colour filter materials, other than glass, fade through use; as the change is gradual, people constantly seeing the lights may become accustomed to the change and not realize that it is taking place until the fade is very marked. It is important to guard against this tendency.

CHAPTER 4

STAGE LIGHTING APPARATUS

THERE is a wide range of lighting equipment available for stage lighting, and much of the apparatus is described and illustrated in the following pages. Further information concerning lay-out will be found in Chapter 7.

FOOTLIGHTS (FLOATS)

In recent years, the open type of footlight, comprising an open trough with white and coloured lamps, has been replaced very largely by the magazine compartment type equipment, in which

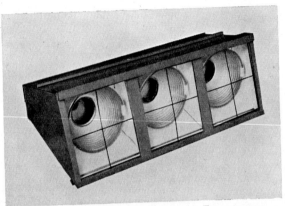

FIG. 18. MAGAZINE COMPARTMENT FOOTLIGHT
(Reproduced by Courtesy of W. J. Furse & Co., Ltd.)

each lamp is located in a separate compartment with its own reflector. The reflectors may be made of silvered or prismatic glass, or constructed of some metal suitably finished, such as anodized aluminium, chromium plated, stainless, or white enamelled steel. The troughing is usually constructed of sheet steel, suitably painted or enamelled, and compartments vary between 6 in. and 10 in. in width, and are fitted with either bayonet cap or Edison screw type lamp holders for use with lamps of between 60 watts and 150 watts in size. Many engineers prefer screw cap lamps, even for the smaller sizes. Clear gas-filled lamps are usually employed because pearl and opal bulbs tend to obstruct light from the reflector, owing to the small size of the compartment opening.

Coloured light is obtained by fitting colour filters in frames in front of the compartments. These filters may be of gelatine or some other non-inflammable and perhaps more durable material, but glass filters are seldom employed as it is difficult to obtain the range of colours required. Sometimes the colour filters have a frosted surface in order to give greater diffusion to the lighting. The colour filter frames usually slide between vertical runners with access from the top, while some form of flap is provided to cover the top aperture when the filters are in position. This flap should be easy to open so that quick and ready access to the filter frames is provided.

One type of footlight equipment employs gelatine or glass roundels that fasten on to the front edge of the circular reflectors. The reflectors can be fitted with 150-watt lamps at 6 in. centres or with 75-watt or 100-watt lamps at 4 in. centres and the apparatus can be arranged so that there are two parallel rows of troughing, one above the other. The upper row projects some 3 in. above the level of the stage floor.

FIG. 19. DOUBLE ROW FOOTLIGHT, UTILIZING GLASS ROUNDELS
(*Reproduced by Courtesy of Major Equipment Co., Ltd.*)

Footlights are usually wired on either three- or four-colour circuits, and sometimes each colour circuit is subdivided into either two or three sections, to give separate control of the middle and ends of each circuit. Thus a footlight may be internally wired on as many as twelve circuits; there should be ample accommodation in the wiring duct for these cables, with proper means of interconnection between adjacent sections of footlight troughing when the cables are not continuous throughout the length of the circuit.

Cinema stage footlights are usually provided with red, green, and blue colour filters, so that a large variety of hues can be obtained by blending these circuits in different proportions. While white light can be obtained by blending red, green, and blue colour circuits together, the intensity is relatively low, and a fourth circuit for white is usually added when the stage is used for theatrical purposes. If the four-colour circuits are controlled by separate dimmers, the footlight is capable of giving any desired colour hues and will provide the necessary colours suitable for curtain effects, as well as

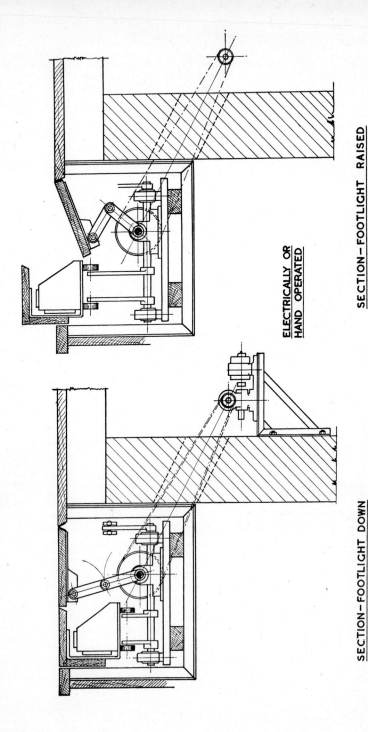

SECTION—FOOTLIGHT DOWN

ELECTRICALLY OR HAND OPERATED

SECTION—FOOTLIGHT RAISED

FIG. 20. ONE TYPE OF DISAPPEARING FOOTLIGHT
(Reproduced by Courtesy of W. J. Furse & Co., Ltd.)

the pastel tints preferred for acting purposes. Three-colour footlights which include white as one of the colours do not give much opportunity for colour mixing. In professional theatres it is still a fairly common practice to fit gelatine colour filters as required for each individual show, and not to standardize. Vaudeville theatres often employ only three circuits, white, red, and blue, in their floats.

FIG. 21. DOUBLE ROW OF FOOTLIGHT EQUIPMENT, EMPLOYING SEMI-CYLINDRICAL COLOUR FILTERS

Generally, footlights should have a distribution of light that will provide good colour mixing on artists and curtains coming near to the equipment. The proscenium curtains are often quite close to the footlights, and care should be taken to obtain a lighting distribution that will remove undue " blobbiness." If the stage is constructed so that artists are liable to come near to the footlights, the light provided by this equipment should be distributed smoothly, so that the light is thrown over the whole body and not mainly on to the lower parts. When the footlights are placed some little distance from the acting area, a concentration of light on the lower part of the stage is sometimes preferred, so that as much light as possible is directed on to the artists. On the other hand, indoor sets of the built-in type with a ceiling have to rely largely on the light given by the footlights for the general illumination of the set, especially of the upper parts, and in these cases a more general distribution of light is desirable.

Many stages, particularly those in concert halls and private theatres, are used for a variety of purposes and do not always

41

require footlights. It is then convenient to mount or construct the footlight equipment so that it can be made to disappear from sight, either by revolving or by lowering into the stage floor. This equipment can be either operated electrically or moved by hand, and the top section becomes part of the stage floor when the apparatus is lowered. The overall height of a footlight—and especially the distance above the lamp filament—is very important, because a footlight normally must project a few inches above the stage floor level in order to cover everything on the stage. As this projection concerns the sight lines from the auditorium ground floor seating to the stage, it is important that it is kept to a minimum. Some footlight equipment is specially designed to cut this projection down as much as possible, but the minimum projection is usually 3 in.

FIG. 22. 250-WATT FLOAT SPOTLIGHT

Special footlight equipment is sometimes constructed so that the lamps can either directly light the stage or be changed in position, so that the light is thrown on to the reflected surface and thence on to the stage. The equipment will thus provide either direct or indirect lighting.

Another type of footlight equipment is an arrangement whereby clear gas-filled lamps are enclosed in semi-cylindrical diffusing type filters at close centres, as shown in Fig. 21. Excellent diffusion and colour mixing from the various circuits is obtained at very near distances, and the equipment can be constructed so that two parallel troughs can be used, giving a total load of 400 watts per foot run with 100-watt lamps at 6 in. centres.

FOOTLIGHT SPOTLIGHTS

Small spotlights are sometimes accommodated between adjacent sections of footlight troughing or in the footlight well. These spotlights are necessarily of very small dimensions and usually employ a 3-in. diameter plano-convex lens and utilize a 100-watt or a 250-watt gas-filled projector lamp.

PROSCENIUM LENGTHS

Trough equipment very similar to footlight troughing is often mounted in vertical lengths behind each side of the proscenium opening. This equipment is usually wired for three- or four-colour circuits for use with lamps up to 150 watts in size. The troughing is best mounted in 6 ft. or other convenient lengths on swivel brackets, so that it may be adjusted in angle to suit varying requirements.

BATTENS

Lengths of magazine compartment troughing similar in nature to the footlights are usually suspended at distances of 6 ft. to 8 ft.

FIG. 23. MAGAZINE COMPARTMENT BATTEN FOR USE WITH 150-WATT LAMPS
(*Reproduced by Courtesy of W. J. Furse & Co., Ltd.*)

apart between the scenic borders. Open type troughs have been superseded almost entirely by magazine compartment equipment, owing to its much greater efficiency, which is very noticeable in the case of overhead battens because of the need for concentration of light in a downward direction. The battens, however, must be capable of lighting a scenic border a short distance away without undue " blobbiness."

The troughing is usually suspended from a length of steel barrel, which is in turn carried by three or four lines; therefore it must be rigid in construction though light in weight, so that it will hang in a straight line and without twisting. The tilt of the trough can be varied on site by adjusting the clamps or hangers that suspend it from the barrel. Battens are often suspended in very close proximity to scenery and border cloths, and the exterior of the troughing should be free from projecting hinges, nuts, boltheads, and so on, that might catch in these objects. This feature facilitates quick scene changing and prevents accidents and damage to the scenery. The trough should be well ventilated, too, so that the exterior of the batten does not get unduly hot: all risk of fire arising from its use must be eliminated.

Batten equipment is usually wired for three- or four-colour circuits and may be subsectioned so that the middle and ends can be controlled separately. This means that there may be as many as twelve circuits in a batten, plus a pilot lamp circuit. It is usual to have two or three lamps in the total length of certain battens on a pilot circuit to provide stage working light. While battens are normally fitted with lamps of 100 watts or 150 watts in size, more powerful equipment is available and lamps of 200 watts or 300 watts can then be utilized in the different compartments.

The internal wiring of a batten terminates at an end connector box and from there flexible tails are usually taken to a junction box on the wall or in another convenient position. The tails, which should include an earthing wire, may comprise separate cables enclosed in suitable hosing or may take the form of a multi-core asbestos braided cable. The tails should be sufficiently long to allow the batten to be lowered to floor level, and if the slack gets in the way when the batten is in its normal position, it can be pulled away by means of a " trick " line.

REVOLVING BATTENS

Colour filter frames for ordinary battens are usually carried between runners in the same manner as with magazine compartment footlights; but there is a type of batten, known as the " revolving batten," in which the colour filter frames are mounted on the periphery of a drum, which is rotatable outside the actual lighting units. Four complete sets of colour filters are usually mounted on this drum, which can be either circular or square in section, and rotation of the drum causes any one of the four sets to come in front of the lighting compartment apertures. The rotation can be obtained by manual operation of ropes and so on, or the equipment can be provided with an electrical mechanism. The purpose of having four complete sets of colour filters is not to produce colour changing effects through rotation of the drum but to cause different sets of selected colours to come in front of the lamps so that operation of lighting circuits will produce different results. For example, one of the four sets of filters may be composed of white, red, green, and blue colours corresponding with four-colour wiring on the lamps, and when these filters are in position the circuits can be blended to give colour-mixing results. The next set of filters on the drum may

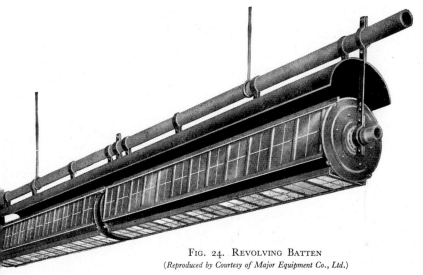

FIG. 24. REVOLVING BATTEN
(*Reproduced by Courtesy of Major Equipment Co., Ltd.*)

be all blue: every lamp in the batten can then be utilized to give blue light when these filters are in position. A third set might be pale amber and a fourth set, say, alternate lavender and yellow.

Revolving battens are suspended in much the same way as ordinary magazine compartment battens, which have to be raised and lowered. It is very important that weight should be kept to a minimum so that the apparatus can be supported from standard suspension equipment and moved by hand without difficulty.

SPOT BATTENS (SPOT BARS)

Lengths of suspension barrel with a number of clamps each carrying a spotlight are often suspended between the scenic borders. Any number of spotlights may be clamped to one barrel according to the needs of the show, but the usual number varies between 10 and 18 spotlights, each for use with one 500-watt or 1000-watt gas-filled projector lamp. Each spotlight can be rotated and tilted so that the light beam can be directed at will, and the spotlight can

45

be detached quickly from the batten if desired. It is usual to wire each spotlight on a separate circuit and to carry the cables either through the inside of the suspension barrel or through another barrel or ducting provided for this purpose and attached to the suspension barrel. Each spotlight is connected to its circuit cables by means of a plug and socket, and the circuit cables terminate in an end connector box from which flexible tails are taken in the same way as in the magazine compartment batten. Any type of spotlight suitable for overhead suspension can be incorporated in the batten. If there is one spot batten on a stage, it is usually fixed near to the proscenium opening, but often an additional spot bar is mounted

FIG. 25. SPOT BATTEN UTILIZING PRISMATIC LENSPLATE SPOTLIGHTS
(*Reproduced by Courtesy of W. J. Furse & Co., Ltd.*)

about mid-stage, or there may even be two or three additional spot battens fixed in convenient positions.

One type of spot batten utilizes spotlights each fitted with a magazine of colour filter frames that are moved into position by means of tracker wires operated from a control board at the side of the stage. In this manner, changes in the colour of the light can be obtained from individual spotlights without having to replace the colour filter frames during a performance. (See Fig. 71.)

FLOOD BATTENS (FLOOD BARS)

These are very similar to the spot battens just described, except that stage floodlights are clamped to the suspension barrel in place of spotlights. Sometimes the equipment fastened to the barrel

46

comprises a number of separate spotlights and floodlights: in this case the equipment is, of course, known as a " spot and flood batten."

The floodlights, usually arranged for use with 500-watt or 1000-watt lamp bulbs, are fitted with glass or metal reflectors, while colour filter frames are fitted conveniently. The design of the reflector determines whether the floodlight gives a narrow, medium, or wide angle distribution of light.

Flood battens for the lighting of cyclorama backgrounds often carry a number of lighting units known as "horizon floods," which give a lighting distribution with a very wide angle, usually up to 180.° Horizon floods are particularly suitable when the cyclorama background is curved, and are sometimes preferred to ordinary floods when the number of lanterns is to be kept to a minimum, as they give good colour mixing results without " blobbiness" when spaced fairly well apart. Generally speaking, however, the high intensity of illumination required on a cyclorama background demands flood lanterns at fairly close centres, and when the background is flat it is often better to employ floods of a more concentrating type, so that most of the light can be directed on to it, provided, of course, that blobbiness is avoided.

FIG. 26. ACTING AREA LANTERN
(Reproduced by Courtesy of R. R. Beard, Ltd.)

Two or even three parallel lengths of magazine compartment batten troughing are sometimes mounted in one framework and suspended as a single unit for the top lighting of a flat cyclorama background. This method gives very good colour mixing from the various colour circuits, owing to the larger number of lamps involved, whereas colour-mixing difficulty is sometimes experienced with a limited number of larger floodlights, especially when they are suspended fairly close to the background.

47

Banks of floodlights are sometimes mounted on a framework in order to build up the necessary lighting intensity for, say, a cyclorama background.

ACTING AREA LANTERNS

Overhead flood lanterns are sometimes required to light portions of the acting area without any appreciable spill of light on to the other parts of the stage. Circular flood lanterns with spill rings or some form of masking attachment at the opening are often used for this purpose and the light is then localized within a stated angle. Ordinary 1000-watt gas-filled lamp bulbs are usually employed, and reflectors are mostly of the concentrating type, made of either metal or silvered glass. Acting area lanterns are usually suspended from a barrel in the same manner as described above for floods and spotlights, and either they may be mixed with a number of these units or there may be sufficient of them to constitute a complete acting area batten.

GROUNDROWS

It is often necessary to utilize portable trough equipment on the stage floor or in the wings, and apparatus similar to stage footlights is usually employed. The apparatus must be of a portable nature and, if at all heavy or difficult to handle, it is usually mounted on wheels. Horizontal groundrows for the lighting of backgrounds, etc., are sometimes mounted in trolleys, and two or even three parallel lengths of equipment employed. The apparatus is normally of the magazine compartment type, utilizing 100-watt or 150-watt gas-filled lamps in reflector compartments at 6 in. to 10 in. centres, but larger lamps are sometimes employed. Particularly when two parallel troughs are in use there is good colour mixing without " blobbiness " at close distances. The length of each groundrow section is usually 6 ft. and each trough or parallel arrangement of troughs is mounted on a trolley and connected either by short tails with plugs to adjacent troughs or directly to some convenient stage plugs.

One type of groundrow utilizes semi-cylindrical diffusing colour filters at 6 in. centres in conjunction with 60-watt or 100-watt lamps. This equipment is very shallow, having a depth of only 3 in., and gives very good colour mixing on surfaces only a few inches away. Clear gas-filled lamps are used behind colour filters and the equipment is usually arranged for either three- or four-colour lighting.

Groundrows are also very useful pieces of apparatus when

mounted vertically, as they can be conveniently accommodated in the wings or behind scenery, and single groundrow troughs are available that are arranged for either horizontal or vertical use.

LENGTHS AND STRIPS

These are usually portable metal channel troughs with lamp holders mounted on the outside at 3 in. or 4 in. centres and wired on various circuits for use with colour-lacquered vacuum lamps.

FIG. 27. 1000-WATT WING FLOOD

No reflectors are employed, as the troughs are usually for use in locations where reflector control is, to a large extent, unnecessary. These channel troughs are also very suitable for use in locations where very little space is available. Lengths of magazine compartment equipment similar to footlights are sometimes called lengths, but these have been described under the heading of Groundrows.

WING FLOODS

Single or multiple wing flood-lighting units are employed in the stage wings to illuminate the acting area and setting. Single wing flood units usually employ a 500-watt or 1000-watt standard gas-filled lamp, and the metal or glass reflector is designed to give either a narrow, medium, or wide angle distribution of light. Runners

49

are provided on the front of the floodlight to carry simultaneously two colour filter frames and it should be possible to push these into position from either side. The floodlight is usually mounted on a portable telescopic stand and is connected by means of flexible cable to a stage plug. Floodlights should be well ventilated and there should be no unwanted leakage of light towards the stage, or colour lighting effects on near surfaces may be marred by blotches of white light. A floodlight should be sturdy in construction but as light as possible, to ensure good portability.

Multiple wing flood equipment may comprise banks of 500-watt or 1000-watt flood units, or groups of magazine compartment reflector units employing smaller lamps. The apparatus is carried in a framework usually mounted on wheels; in the case of magazine troughing it can be tilted on one horizontal axis. When a number of 500-watt or 1000-watt flood units are employed, these are sometimes mounted as separate units above each other in the framework, and in this case each flood can be individually tilted and directed. When the flood units are assembled together in one bank this is not possible and the group of flood units is then tilted or directed as one unit. Sometimes two vertical rows of four 500-watt flood units are mounted in parallel. Multiple flood equipment is often arranged on three- or four-colour circuits so that colour blending effects can be provided.

PROJECTOR LAMP SPOTLIGHTS

Spotlights employing gas-filled lamps play an important part in stage lighting, and there is a variety of types and sizes, which may be classified mainly as follows—

(A) SPOTLIGHTS EMPLOYING A PLANO-CONVEX LENS. The lanterns are usually made in four sizes and are fitted with lenses as follows—

SIZE OF LAMP	LENS
100–250 watts	3 in. diameter × 6 in. focus
500 watts	4½ in. diameter × 6½ in. focus 6 in. diameter × 10 in. focus
1000 watts	6 in. diameter × 10 in. focus
2000 watts	8 in. diameter × 13 in. focus

The 500-watt spotlight is usually known as the " baby " spotlight, and the smaller size as a " miniature " or " footlight " spot. The 1000-watt spotlight is regarded as the standard size and the 2000-watt model as a larger spotlight.

Circular spherical type reflectors made of either metal or glass are employed and the reflector diameter is either the same or slightly less than the diameter of the lens. The reflector is usually

FIG. 28. MULTI-COLOUR WING FLOOD
TROLLEY UNIT
(*Reproduced by Courtesy of W. J. Furse & Co., Ltd.*)

FIG. 29. TRIPLE WING FLOOD UNIT
(*Reproduced by Courtesy of R. R. Beard, Ltd.*)

mounted on the same tray as the lamp holder, so that both are moved as one unit when focus of the spotlight has to be altered.

(*B*) LENSLESS SPOTLIGHTS. Narrow beam spotlights are available which in place of a lens employ an open front fitted with circular spill rings. Nearly all of the light is derived from a parabolic

FIG. 30. 2000-WATT STAGE SPOTLIGHT FITTED WITH PLANO-CONVEX LENS
(*Reproduced by Courtesy of R. R. Beard, Ltd.*)

reflector at the rear of the lamp bulb, as the spill rings are constructed to allow the reflected light rays to pass through, while the direct light from the lamp is trapped and prevented from escaping outside the angle of the reflected beam. This type is useful when high intensity narrow angle beams of light are required. There is a fairly sharp cut-off and little spill of light outside the actual beam angle. These narrow angle spotlights are generally for use with 500-watt or 1000-watt gas-filled projector lamps and the spill ring aperture is about 10 in. wide. Mirror glass reflectors are usually employed but metal reflectors also are available, and have the advantage of being unbreakable.

(C) PRISMATIC LENSPLATE SPOTLIGHTS. A soft-edged beam of light is provided by spotlights that utilize a prismatic step lens. This

FIG. 31. LENSLESS SPOTLIGHT, UTILIZING SPILL RINGS IN CONJUNCTION
WITH PARABOLIC REFLECTOR
(Reproduced by Courtesy of W. J. Furse & Co., Ltd.)

type of lens is more efficient than the plano-convex lens and is capable of a much wider variation of beam angle. The spotlight gives a high intensity soft-edged beam, which can be varied in width, usually with a main beam divergence of 5° to 45°; it therefore combines the qualities of both spot and flood lanterns because the focusing mechanism provides a concentrated beam when a spot is required, and a wide angle beam up to 45° when floodlighting is necessary. A 10-in. diameter prismatic step lens is usually

53

employed in conjunction with an 8½-in. diameter reflector, and 500-watt or 1000-watt gas-filled projector lamps Class A1 and B1 or 2000-watt bi-post lamps can be utilized with this arrangement. A 6-in. diameter prismatic step lens is sometimes employed in a smaller body for use with 500-watt and 1000-watt lamps.

(D) Mirror Spotlights With Variable Gate. One type of

Fig. 32. Frenca Spotlight, Utilizing 10-in. diam. Prismatic Lensplate
(*Reproduced by Courtesy of W. J. Furse & Co., Ltd.*)

spotlight uses an 8-in. diameter silvered glass reflector in conjunction with a variable aperture and front step lens, and the optical system is designed so that, by means of adjustable slides and shutters, the light beam can be altered in shape to suit requirements. Shaped beams can thus be obtained and the spotlight can be adjusted so that uneven areas on the stage can be accurately lighted without spill. The equipment is normally designed for use with a 1000-watt lamp.

(E) Spotlights With Ellipsoidal Reflectors. Another type

of spotlight uses ellipsoidal reflectors in conjunction with a stepped lens positioned behind a front lens, and this spot, in conjunction with an iris diaphragm, vertical and horizontal shutters, enables the size and shape of the spot to be varied at will. A 30-volt 30-ampere 900-watt lamp is frequently employed. This type of spotlight has a very high lighting efficiency, and is powerful enough to be used for front-of-house spot work.

Low voltage lamp bulbs, as for example the 12-volt 36-watt headlight lamp, can be utilized in spotlights, and are suitable for the five classes just described, when they are designed for this purpose.

These low voltage lamp bulbs are much smaller in size than ordinary gas-filled lamps and can be accommodated in a smaller lantern. Furthermore, the filament can be brought closer to the lens, enabling a small lens to control a reasonable angle of light flux. The filament of a low voltage lamp is also more compact, giving a better focus, and the lumen output per watt is higher than in the case of normal voltage lamps. This greater efficiency compensates for any transformer losses and, in conjunction with the compact filament shape, gives a very effective light for a low consumption of electricity.

Small spotlights, fitted with a prismatic step lens (see Class C above) and utilizing small standard voltage bulbs, are used considerably in America. The beam is soft-edged and the angle can be widely varied, while the intensity of the light is sufficiently strong for many stage purposes. They are frequently used in overhead positions or operated from spot bars, and are also conveniently housed on booms in the wings and at the sides of the proscenium arch.

Transformers are usually employed to provide the low voltage supply, and these, of course, can be used only on A.C. mains.

The prismatic step lens spotlight (see Class C above), using normal voltage lamps up to 2000 watts in size, is now coming very much into favour, and is particularly suitable for use in general stage work, because of its very high efficiency, soft-edged beam, and widely variable beam angle.

PERCH SPOTLIGHTS AND FLOODLIGHTS

One or more spotlights are usually mounted on a perch platform at either side of the proscenium opening. Arc spotlights are employed when it is desired to " pin-point " an artist from the sides; in fact, until recent years, projector lamp type spotlights were not considered strong enough for general use on the perches. The greater efficiency of modern spotlights, however, enables projector lamp type equipment to be utilized on a number of stages, although it is still difficult to " pin-point " with a high intensity beam unless an arc spotlight is employed. Prismatic lensplate spotlights, however, give a light beam of relatively high efficiency that is also variable in width, and they are very suitable for giving general illumination from a perch platform, although they are not suitable for a sharp focus.

In the past, there has been a tendency to rely on perch spotlights to a considerable extent for the actual illumination of the artists, but modern stage lighting installations provide essential illumination from many other positions, so that it is no longer necessary to " follow " an artist from the perches, except to obtain a desired effect. Instead, it is fairly common practice to mount a number of spotlights or floodlights on the perch platforms and to set these for the show, in much the same manner as with batten spotlights. Standard spotlights and floodlights then are employed, according to the needs of the lighting plot.

SPOT AND FLOOD BOOMS

Spotlights are sometimes mounted one above the other on vertical barrels or other suitable mountings known as booms, or boomerangs. These booms are usually mounted in the wings near the front of the stage, and are sometimes accommodated immediately behind the sides of the proscenium opening. The spotlights are usually of a very compact type, taking up the minimum of space, and are often set for the whole show. When the boom is portable, however, or easily accessible in the wings, the various spotlights may be adjusted for different scenes. Sometimes the spotlights are fitted with a magazine of colour filters, which are moved into position by tracker wires operated from control levers in the stage wings.

Boomerangs carrying a number of floodlights are sometimes accommodated in the stage wings.

SPOT AND FLOOD TOWERS

Movable towers for use in stage wings are often constructed and fitted with a number of individual spotlights and floodlights, as required. These towers may be as high as 24 ft. and have one or more platforms on which an operator can stand. The towers are moved into position when required, and in this manner the lighting equipment is quickly positioned and can be speedily removed from the wings when no longer required. These towers are designed to suit individual requirements and constitute a very useful addition to a stage lighting installation.

ARC SPOTLIGHTS

Theatre arc spotlights vary very considerably in design and range from a simple 15–20-amp. arc spotlight with a two-movement hand feed to an elaborate 120-amp. projector, fitted with a six-movement feed and vertical and horizontal barn-door shutters, iris

Fig. 33. Arc Spotlight, Utilizing Plano-convex Lens
(Reproduced by Courtesy of R. R. Beard, Ltd.)

diaphragm, colour magazine, and change-over lenses. Most of the spotlights actually used on a theatre stage (except for effect projectors) are of a simple type, employing a three-movement hand feed arc mechanism for an arc current of 20–30 amps., and the more elaborate types of equipment employed mostly for front-of-house spot work.

When used on a stage, arc spotlights are usually positioned on the perch platforms or are located on the stage for use with special effects attachments. They are rarely used for ordinary wing lighting. Perch arc spotlights usually employ a 6-in. diameter

57

FIG. 34. FRONT-OF-HOUSE MAGAZINE 80-AMP. ARC PROJECTOR
(*Reproduced by Courtesy of R. R. Beard, Ltd.*)

plano-convex lens with an open scissors type arc mechanism without a reflector. A D.C. supply of approximately 50 volts is employed and good results are obtained on 15–30 amps. In recent years A.C. carbons have become available which enable good results to be obtained on an A.C. supply of 25 volts.

Similar apparatus, usually fitted with a double plano-convex lens, is available for use with optical effects attachments, but for a large

FIG. 35. EFFECTS PROJECTOR
(*Reproduced by Courtesy of R R. Beard, Ltd*).

stage, or an installation where there is a high standard of general illumination, a larger type of projector, taking up to 50–60 amperes, may be employed.

Front-of-house type spotlights vary considerably in type and size, according to the length of throw and the required intensity. When the spotlights are mounted in the auditorium at positions near to the stage, 30–40-amp. projectors of a simple type may be suitable; but when the projectors are mounted at the rear of the auditorium or project their beam through openings in the dome, etc., 60–80-amp. equipment may be necessary, and in certain cases

59

apparatus taking up to 120 amps. Front-of-house type spotlights are usually fitted with a 6-in. diameter, heat-resisting plano-convex lens, with a six-movement hand feed type arc mechanism. The lantern usually carries an iris diaphragm operated by a hand-wheel at the rear and also vertical and horizontal barn door shutters similarly controlled. A magazine containing four- or six-colour filter frames is often mounted on the front, and these frames are operated by tracker wires or chains from handles at the back of the lamp-house.

A more elaborate type of equipment is available and includes a

FIG. 36. EFFECTS ATTACHMENT FOR MOUNTING ON SPOTLIGHT PROJECTOR
(*Reproduced by Courtesy of Major Equipment Co., Ltd.*)

FIG. 37. COMBINATION OF SEA AND CLOUD EFFECTS
(*Reproduced by Courtesy of Major Equipment Co., Ltd.*)

lamp-house and mirror arc mechanism similar to that of a cinematograph projector. The area and shape of the light beam can be controlled at will and effects attachments can be included to give moving colour effects.

EFFECTS PROJECTORS AND ATTACHMENTS

The effect of moving clouds, lightning, rain, smoke, fire, etc., can be obtained by fitting special effects attachments on to spotlight projectors specially made for this work. The spotlight is usually fitted with a double plano-convex condenser lens and can be used with either a 1000-watt gas-filled projector lamp or with an arc mechanism. It is necessary also to use an objective lens in addition to the condenser lens but the former is usually carried in a separate mounting placed on the other side of the effects attachment, which is carried in runners in front of the condenser lens. The projector lantern and the objective lens can thus be used with any suitable effects attachment that is mounted, the angle of the final beam depending upon the type of objective lens.

A separate effect attachment is usually required for each illusion, so that fire, smoke, clouds, etc., each require a different attachment. The apparatus generally incorporates a clockwork motor to provide the necessary movement, but sometimes an electric drive is mounted.

FIG. 38. BALCONY SPOTLIGHT FITTED WITH ELECTRICALLY OPERATED
COLOUR FILTERS
(*Reproduced by Courtesy of W. J. Furse & Co., Ltd.*)

If there is a high intensity of stage illumination adjacent to the area to be lighted from the effects projector, it may be necessary to use the arc type, and two or more projectors may be needed to cover the required area.

Ultra-violet glass filters can be fitted on to arc spotlights and then only objects treated with fluorescent paints will be visible. Fluorescent paint can be applied to scenery and costumes and some very striking effects can be arranged. Ultra-violet light also can be obtained from a standard 125-watt black bulb (see page 32).

61

Fluorescent paint is obtainable in a number of colours, including red, orange, yellow, green, peacock blue, blue, magenta, and pink, and some of these colours cannot be seen under white light.

BALCONY FRONT SPOTLIGHTS

Spotlights employing gas-filled projector lamps are often mounted on the front edge of a circle or balcony. The spotlights are often of a special design to facilitate access to the lamp, etc., and the size is kept to a minimum. 1000-watt gas-filled lamps are usually

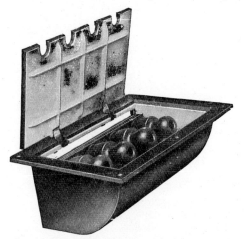

FIG. 39. 4-WAY STAGE DIP BOX WITH PLUGS
(*Reproduced by Courtesy of R. R. Beard, Ltd.*)

employed, but some installations include spotlights employing 1500-watt and 2000-watt lamps. Plano-convex lenses are often used, but the prismatic lensplate is coming into use because of its greater efficiency and soft-edged beam of light.

When light from the spotlights tends to spill into the orchestra pit or auditorium, special masking attachments are fitted that restrict the light within the stage opening. One type of mirror spotlight includes an optical system that allows the shape of the beam to be varied at will so that uneven areas can be lighted.

An electrically operated colour filter mechanism is often mounted on the front of each spotlight, so that the colours can be changed by remote control. The movement of the colour filter frames is usually provided by electric solenoids, which are smooth and silent in operation and easy to maintain. Each spotlight is generally fitted with either three or four electrically operated filters and each of these is controlled by a separate switch on a stage control panel. The solenoid coils in most equipments require a D.C. supply, and when the only electrical supply available is A.C., the necessary D.C. supply is usually obtained from a rectifier or motor-generator.

FLOOR STANDS

Portable spotlights and floodlights are usually mounted on telescopic floor stands, and it is important that suitable stands are utilized or the equipment may be top-heavy. The standard light type floor stand extends to 5 ft. 6 in. and the standard heavy type extends to 7 ft. in height and has a weight of approximately 40 lb. These stands are sometimes mounted on rubber-tyred castors, but care must be taken on a raked stage to see that the stands do not move down stage of their own accord. Special ball runners that will obviate this tendency can be fitted to the underneath of stands for use on a raked stage. (See also page 50.)

Tripod stands are often employed in place of single telescopic stands and these extend to about the same height. They can be mounted on wheels or roller balls. Extra high stands are available that extend to 10 ft. or 12 ft. and it is usual to place stage weights on to the base legs to steady them in position.

Stands are often fitted with a rack to carry spare colour-filter frames, and this is a very useful arrangement.

Cables from portable lighting equipment usually terminate in connecting plugs fitting into sockets mounted either in a recess below the stage floor (see Fig. 39) or on some convenient surface such as a wall.

This chapter is not intended to be a complete catalogue of every type and arrangement of stage lighting apparatus, but describes much of the equipment in general use.

CHAPTER 5

DIMMERS AND LIGHTING CONTROL EQUIPMENT

THE success and workability of a stage lighting installation depend to a very considerable extent on the lighting control apparatus. A clever or elaborate lighting system is of little use unless the installation can be manipulated as required under normal working conditions. The dimmer switchboard or other control apparatus provided must, therefore, be flexible enough to meet the many different demands that may be made on it.

PURCHASE OF SUITABLE CONTROL APPARATUS

When a given sum is available for the whole installation, there is a tendency to spend too large a proportion on the lighting equipment and to over-simplify the dimmer switchboard. It is often wiser to plan an installation so that the switchboard is fundamentally right in the first place and can, together with a modest amount of lighting apparatus, be used with good results, further lighting and dimmer equipment being added to the installation as finance permits. Additional switch and dimmer circuits can be added to a dimmer switchboard if reasonable provision is made in the first place.

Dramatic lighting effects depend to a considerable extent on variations of lighting intensity from different directions, and dimmers are required to vary the brightness of circuits to the required degree. Dimmers are also utilized for the colour blending of different circuits in multi-colour lighting equipment to obtain a desired colour hue. These functions are often more important than the slow reduction of stage lighting from brightness to blackout and vice versa, and dimming installations should seldom be considered with undue emphasis on the latter.

MINIMUM NUMBER OF DIMMERS

The ideal arrangement is to have a separate dimmer on every stage lighting circuit, together with means for collective operation of these dimmers in any required manner. When this is not possible, the number of dimmers to be provided should be calculated with the following points well in mind—

(*a*) It should be possible to dim lighting equipment at each side of the stage independently from the other side.

(*b*) Footlights should be on separate dimmers from overhead lighting battens.

(*c*) When perch spotlights are controlled by dimmers, each side should be operated independently.

(*d*) Auditorium projector-lamp spotlights, which light the stage from widely different angles, should be on independent dimmers.

It is possible for a dimmer to be utilized for the control of circuits in two or more sets of lighting equipment, provided the dimmer is designed to give satisfactory results on the minimum and maximum loads thus entailed, but it is generally wiser to provide separate circuit switches for each set of lighting equipment. Thus, if there are four four-colour overhead lighting battens, it would be possible to control these on eight dimmers by putting No. 1 and 2 battens on four dimmers and No. 3 and 4 battens on further dimmers, but there should be four circuit switches for each batten, making a total of sixteen switches for the eight dimmers. Each lighting circuit should, of course, be provided also with separate fuses.

LAY-OUT OF DIMMER EQUIPMENT

When grouping dimmers in rows or tiers, it is usual to arrange for all lighting circuits normally giving the same colour to be controlled by dimmers in the same row. Four-colour battens and footlights are then controlled by four banks of dimmers, one for each of the four sets of colours. Thus, a row of dimmers has come to be regarded as a colour row, and a dimmer switchboard with three or four banks of dimmers is usually known as a three- or four-colour board, even though a number of dimmers in each row may have nothing to do with any particular colour. A four-colour board can be arranged, however, with a height of only two tiers, by having two rows of dimmers parallel with the other two rows.

The switches controlling the dimmer circuits are classified likewise; when there is a master switch for each row of circuit switches, it is usually known as a colour master switch. Circuit switches should be mounted whenever possible so that each switch is located in line with the dimmer it controls.

In addition to an adequate number of circuit switches and dimmers, provision must also be made to enable groups of switches and dimmers to be operated collectively. The degree to which this is done varies considerably, but there must always be means of giving a complete black-out by a master switch, and, if possible, provision for collective operation of all the dimmers for a master dim-out. Colour master and grand master switch and dimmer controls will be discussed in detail later in this chapter, together with special

65

types of lighting control apparatus that have been developed to deal with the problems of multiple operation.

The electrical load of a stage lighting installation, even in a small private theatre, is usually too heavy to be accommodated by an electrical supply undertaking on a two-wire main supply (unless the public supply itself is only two-wire); in most cases it is necessary to balance the load across two or three phases when the public supply is A.C. or across the outers of a three-wire supply when this is D.C. This means that in the case of a 230–400-volt A.C. supply or 200–400-volt D.C. supply, there is a potential of 400 volts between certain dimmers, switches, and fuses. The operator must be protected, always, from any possibility of receiving a shock from a voltage of this nature, and the control apparatus must be arranged accordingly. When the dimmers, etc., are mounted with live parts not wholly protected they should not be handled directly by an operator when on balanced loads, unless dimmers on the different phases or sides of the supply are grouped at least 6 ft. 6 in. apart. It is usually impracticable to lay out an installation on these lines, so in the case of balanced loads, dead front type equipment as described in the following pages is utilized. Alternatively, the dimmers are suitably mounted and protected and are operated from remote handles.

TYPES OF DIMMERS

A dimmer (sometimes called a resistance or rheostat) is a device for reducing the light given by an electric lamp by means of a reduction in the voltage of the circuit. Dimmers vary very considerably in design and construction but the majority of dimmers in use to-day rely on the use of a moving contact arm, which varies the amount of resistance wire in series with the lamp circuit. These are conveniently called wire wound dimmers and may be of a slider, radial, or rotary type. Liquid dimmers were used to a considerable extent in the past, but are now largely obsolete, having been replaced mainly by the wire-wound dimmer.

A dimmer that has aroused considerable interest in some quarters is known as the reactance dimmer. This operates on a different principle from the wire-wound type, as it works on the basis of electrical reactance, employing a variable choke or electronic valve to control the voltage. This type of dimmer should not be confused with the auto-transformer type, which also gives very good results on an A.C. supply.

These various types of dimmers will be discussed in further detail in the following pages.

66

LIQUID DIMMERS

A liquid dimmer comprises a glazed earthenware jar (containing water partly saturated with special salts) and a pair of contact plates, one of which is fixed at the bottom of the jar and the other suspended from the end of a tracker wire or rod. By increasing and decreasing the distance in the liquid between the fixed and movable contact plates, a dimming effect is obtained. The apparatus is quite simple and the liquid dimmer has the virtue that it will dim effectively a variable load up to its maximum capacity without flicker.

It is subject, however, to certain disadvantages, such as the continued evaporation of the water and the bulkiness of the equipment. The liquid requires constant attention to ensure that the solution is kept at the same strength, while corrosion is apt to take place on metal parts adjacent to the liquid. These disadvantages have outweighed the advantages, and to-day the liquid dimmer is almost obsolete in modern stage installations.

SLIDER TYPE DIMMERS

This type of dimmer is not expensive and is used to a considerable extent for loads up to about 3000 watts, but for larger loads the dimmer becomes rather bulky and often gets a little difficult for hand operation when left in check for any time, owing to the heat that is generated.

A slider dimmer consists essentially of a sliding contact brush movable along the surface of a graduated resistance winding made up of nickel chrome or nickel copper resistance wire wound upon an insulated former. This winding is in series at one end with the lamp circuit and elsewhere with the movable contact brush, the position of which along the winding determines the amount of resistance wire in series with the lamp circuit.

In order to give a good dimming, it is usual to wind portions of each resistance in different gauges of resistance wire, and it is important that the change in size between adjacent windings is not too marked or a ridge may be created and the contact brush will tend to cut the wire at this point. A quick break switch is usually fitted at the " dim-out " end of the dimmer to prevent arcing at the end of the stroke. The bar on which the contact arm slides should be well insulated, and the external covers constructed so that in spite of the slot through which the operating knob projects, it is difficult to make contact from the outside with the windings or other live parts of the dimmer.

67

From the point of view of good dimming, the slider type dimmer is one of the best available, because it gives flickerless dimming and has a smooth action. When a number of dimmers are mounted side by side, however, it is difficult to get group control direct from the dimmer knobs, and furthermore, if adjacent dimmers are con-

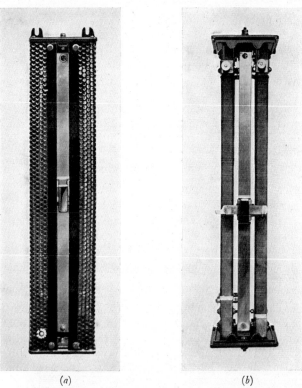

(a)   (b)

FIG. 40. SLIDER TYPE DIMMER (a) WITH AND (b) WITHOUT PROTECTIVE
COVERS

nected on different phases of an A.C. supply or across the outers of a three-wire D.C. supply, it is inadvisable to operate them directly by hand. Both of these disadvantages can be overcome, however, by mounting the dimmers in a framework and operating them by means of tracker wires from control wheels suitably mounted on a master shafting.

Slider dimmers should be made so that they can be left in check for long periods without getting unduly hot, and the sliding contact assembly designed so that it is not stiff to operate when the dimmer temperature rises. Most standard slider dimmers can be adapted for worm-screw operation, whereby the contact arm moves by rotation of a centre shaft. This type of action permits the whole of a dimmer to be enclosed, and then it is possible to arrange for a number of adjacent resistances to be used on a balanced supply,

FIG. 41. RADIAL LEVER DIMMER
(Reproduced by Courtesy of W. J. Furse & Co., Ltd.)

and simultaneously operated from one master handle. Slider dimmers, in common with all resistance wire dimmers, will give good results only when used with a load that approximates that for which they were designed; they are not suitable for use with widely varying loads.

RADIAL LEVER DIMMERS

With this type of dimmer the contact arm is pivoted so that the contact brush moves in an arc instead of sliding in a straight line

69

as with the slider type dimmer. The resistance wire is usually mounted in the framework in the form of a number of separate coils or lengths of wire wound on small formers, and each resistance element is connected to a separate stud, so that the contact brush moves over a series of studs. The radial stud type dimmer can usually be wound for loads up to 25 amps., which means 5000 watts on a 200-volt supply. The number of contact studs provided varies with different makes of dimmer, but the minimum is usually about 60 studs and the maximum 150. The majority of radial stud type dimmers employ between 80 and 110 contact studs.

FIG. 42. ROTARY TYPE DIMMER
(*Reproduced by Courtesy of Major Equipment Co., Ltd.*)

Even with 80 steps of resistance, it is difficult to get a slow dimming change that is completely free from jumps in the lighting throughout the whole range; some people hold that 150 contact studs are required to give a really flickerless dim-out. For most general purposes, however, 80 or 100 contact stud dimmers give adequate results and are reasonably free from flicker, except perhaps at the dim-out end of the travel.

While radial lever type dimmers are usually fitted with contact studs, there is another type in which the contact brush actually moves over the resistance winding in much the same manner as with a slider dimmer, except that a curved path is traversed. This type of radial dimmer gives the same flickerless dimming as that obtained from the slider dimmer, and can be wound for loads up to about 15 amps. An example of this type of dimmer is shown in Fig. 41.

Radial lever dimmers are very suitable for dead front type dimmer switchboards, because the dimmers can be mounted behind the operating panel and the contact arm connected by means of a rod or link to an operating handle on the front of the board. In this manner, a number of radial dimmers can be mounted side by side and used on a balanced electricity supply, without any special protection and without danger to the operator, provided, of course, that the dimmers are totally enclosed within the main framework. Some radial dimmers have a double arm with a contact brush at each end, and this type of resistance is frequently employed as a variable arc resistance for use with carbon arc spotlights.

ROTARY TYPE DIMMERS

This type of dimmer is similar in many ways to the radial type, except that the contact studs are mounted in a circle and the contact arm rotates through a greater angle. The resistance wires are suitably bedded in the space that lies within the circle of contact studs, and a totally enclosed dimmer can be created in which all live parts and resistance wires are shut in completely and protected from external contact or damage. Rotary motion can be given to the dimmer arm by mounting it on a centre shaft and turning this by a rack and pinion mechanism.

FIG. 43. INTERIOR OF ROTARY TYPE DIMMER
(*Reproduced by Courtesy of Major Equipment Co., Ltd.*)

This dimmer has the advantages that a large number of contact studs can be conveniently incorporated in a space with a moderate width, and the dimmer windings and contacts are totally enclosed.

AUTO-TRANSFORMER DIMMERS

The dimmers so far described require to operate on a load approximating to the normal rating of the dimmer in order to give proper dimming results. The Auto-transformer type of dimmer, however, will give almost uniform dimming with a load varying from a few watts to the maximum load of the dimmer.

The dimmer is in effect a multi-tapped transformer connected directly across the A.C. mains, and is designed so that its impedance keeps the current to a low value. The transformer winding is tapped at numerous positions, either by giving each turn of the winding a bare surface to give contact to a movable brush or by connecting the winding to a number of contact studs.

The lamp load is connected between one side of the electric supply and the movable contact brush. Movement of the brush controls the voltage supplied to the lamps. This voltage is determined by the transformer action of the control apparatus and not by the actual lamp load. Each lamp will therefore give a uniform brightness at any contact point and is unaffected by any changes in the load of the circuit.

Auto-transformer dimmers are constructed in many compact shapes which lend themselves to mounting at close centres, and the contact arm can move with a rotary or straight action. This type of equipment is, of course, only suitable for use on A.C. supply.

ELECTRONIC REACTOR DIMMERS

With the Electronic reactor dimmer the lamp load is connected in series with the A.C. winding of a saturable reactor, which embodies also another winding that is supplied with D.C. current from a special form of rectifier known as an electronic valve rectifier. The output of D.C. current from the rectifier is controlled by a small potentiometer device, which governs the voltage applied to the grid circuit of this rectifier valve. The impedance of the A.C. winding in the reactor is normally sufficient to keep the current down to a point when the lamps are dimmed completely, but when the D.C. saturating current is employed, the impedance of the A.C. winding is reduced, and when the D.C. current is increased to a certain strength the lamps can operate at full light.

The movement of the potentiometer control varies the amount of D.C. current in the reactor and thus the brightness of the lamps can usually be varied on 25 per cent to 100 per cent of full load without affecting the dimming results, and when the lights are wholly or partly dimmed there is not the usual consumption of electricity experienced with ordinary resistance dimmers.

The electronic reactor dimmer is fundamentally suitable for remote control work, and owing to the small size of the potentiometer device that controls the brightness of the lamps, a large amount of apparatus can be manipulated from quite a small control panel. Controls for pre-setting a number of scenes and providing group or master action of both switch and dimmer equipment can be added in a very moderate space.

D.C. CONTROLLED REACTOR DIMMERS

Reactor dimmer equipment can, of course, be arranged to work in conjunction with a suitable D.C. supply controlled by an ordinary type of dimmer or rheostat instead of electronic valves. In this manner large dimmer loads can be controlled by small resistance dimmers mounted in the stage switchboard framework, while the actual reactor dimmers are accommodated elsewhere.

ELECTRONIC VALVE DIMMERS

Rapid development of electronic valves during the past few years has added yet another type of dimmer that is available in theatre lighting use to-day. Valves capable of directly handling

FIG. 44. PORTABLE SLIDER DIMMER SWITCHBOARD

lighting loads have been developed and are being used in a variety of different types of commercially available stage lighting equipment in both Europe and America. At the present time loads up to 2000 watts may be controlled by a single valve in Europe, while in the U.S.A. valves are available to handle up to 4000 watts each. A point to remember in connexion with electronic dimmers is that the valves themselves are expendable. Therefore, a maintenance budget for the equipment must be considered.

PORTABLE AND SLIDER TYPE DIMMER
SWITCHBOARDS

Dimmer switchboards that employ slider type dimmers may be grouped into two main classes : (a) where the dimmer resistances are directly manipulated by hand, and (b) where the resistances are mounted inside a framework and are moved by operating

73

handles mounted apart from the dimmers. A typical example of a slider dimmer board of the first class is shown in Fig. 44, which is a portable board and very suitable for touring. The wooden framework carries twelve slider type dimmers and each is controlled by a separate circuit switch and pair of porcelain fuses. A pilot lamp circuit is provided and the equipment is wired up internally to a pair of main terminals. A plug socket is provided with each dimmer circuit, so that cables from the different pieces of lighting equipment can be easily connected. Touring type dimmer switchboards are often constructed so that a wooden front can be screwed quickly into position to protect the switches, fuses, etc., from damage during transit.

Slider dimmer type switchboards are also constructed for permanent installations, and of course vary in size and lay-out according to individual requirements. The dimensions of a sliding dimmer vary according to the load it is constructed to carry, and the lay-out of a switchboard is often governed by the varying sizes of the dimmers. Portable dimmer switchboards are normally fitted throughout with 500-watt or 1000-watt dimmers as standard.

Dimmer switchboards of this kind are probably the least expensive to construct, but they are subject to the disadvantage that it is difficult to arrange for the dimmers to be both individually and collectively operated as desired, especially when the dimmers vary in length. A master dim-out is thus difficult to obtain unless some ingenuity is exercised. Furthermore, it is advisable, and in some areas compulsory, to keep all adjacent slider type dimmers on a two-wire main supply when this is D.C., or on a single phase when it is A.C., as the open slot in the front of a slider dimmer partly exposes parts that are electrically alive.

Every switchboard should be controlled by a grand master black-out switch, which, if not actually mounted upon it, should be fixed in an adjacent position.

The limitations just mentioned can be overcome if a dimmer switchboard of the type shown in Fig. 45 is used, because the actual dimmer resistances are not exposed, and movement is provided by operating handles away from the actual dimmers. The dimmer circuits can then be balanced over different phases of an A.C. supply or across the outers of a three-wire D.C. supply without risk. Each dimmer is actuated by steel tracker wires connected to a hand-wheel on top of the framework. These hand-wheels are all mounted on one shaft and the operating handles are of the twist-grip type, enabling one or more to be locked to the shaft and collectively operated by a master hand-wheel as desired. Collective operation

74

of all the dimmers is thus possible and a master dim-out can be obtained with ease.

This type of dimmer switchboard is very suitable for touring work, as the boards are portable and can be mounted on wheels. Touring boards are made in two standard sizes, having six and

FIG. 45. PORTABLE INTERLOCKING TYPE DIMMER SWITCHBOARD
(Reproduced by Courtesy of W. J. Furse & Co., Ltd.)

twelve dimmer circuits respectively, and each circuit is complete with switch, pair of fuses, plug, and socket. A master black-out switch can be mounted on the framework and the board is complete, usually, with a pilot lamp circuit. This type of equipment can, of course, be made up to control any desired number of dimmers.

When all the operating hand-wheels are of the same size, as shown in the illustration, it is necessary for the dimmers all to have the same length of travel or a master dim-out becomes rather difficult. But when different dimmer lengths are inevitable, this disadvantage can be overcome by using operating wheels of different diameters, so that each handle travels the same distance from " full-on " to " dim-out."

Tracker wire type dimmer switchboards can be constructed in many different ways and sometimes the actual dimmers are mounted in a room over or under the one that contains the operating handles. Sometimes the dimmers are mounted on the wall above the actual switchboard, and dimmer operating handles and arrangements of this nature allow for economy in valuable space.

DEAD FRONT DIMMER SWITCHBOARDS

This type of dimmer switchboard is the one usually employed in permanent stage installations because, as the name implies, all dimmers and live parts are protected and the apparatus can be used with safety on three-phase A.C. and three-wire D.C. supplies.

The dimmers are of the radial lever or rotary type mounted in tiers and connected by means of toggle links to operating handles on the front of the board. These operating handles may be of the twist-grip type, or have special clutches that enable any desired number of them to be locked to the shafting on which they are mounted and collectively operated by means of a master hand-wheel.

In some cases dimmer operating handles are provided with special clutches that release a handle when it has reached the end of its travel.

Dead front type dimmer boards vary considerably in size and lay-out according to the size of the installation. In the professional theatre the number of dimmer ways might average sixty, but in private theatre installations a more usual number is twenty-four. Cinema stage installations vary considerably and in the case of ciné-variety theatres may have a switchboard equal in size to that of the professional theatre.

Certain features are, however, generally common to most dead front dimmer boards, e.g. grouping of the dimmers in the lower half and circuit switches on panels above the dimmers. The fuse panels are often mounted at the top of the board but are sometimes fixed at the side or back of the framework.

Two, three, or four dimmer tiers may be mounted above each other, but four is considered the maximum, or the board becomes too high for convenient operation of the circuit switches above. Each horizontal row of dimmers, however, may be divided into sections, each with its own master hand-wheel. Each bank of dimmers may be provided with a separate slow motion worm drive, but this should be so arranged that the worm-wheel can be quickly

FIG. 46. DEAD FRONT TYPE FOUR-COLOUR DIMMER SWITCHBOARD
(*Reproduced by Courtesy of W. J. Furse & Co., Ltd.*)

disengaged and the master shafting operated by its own hand-wheel so that quick group action is possible.

FIG. 47. BACK VIEW OF DEAD FRONT TYPE DIMMER SWITCHBOARD
SHOWING MOUNTING OF DIMMERS

A convenient lay-out for a large dimmer switchboard is to arrange the dimmers in four tiers, one above the other, and to divide each tier into two separate halves with master and slow

FIG. 48. GRAND MASTER CROSS CONTROL MECHANISM FOR DEAD
FRONT TYPE DIMMER SWITCHBOARD
(*Reproduced by Courtesy of W. J. Furse & Co., Ltd.*)

motion hand-wheels in the centre of the board. In this way eight banks of dimmers are accommodated, each with its own drive, and grand master control can be mounted in the centre. When a grand master hand-wheel is available to rotate one or more of the master dimmer shafts in the same direction, so that any desired number of dimmers can be raised or lowered together, then the master drive is known as "Grand Master Control." When, however, the grand master gear is arranged so that any master dimmer shaft can be connected to rotate in the same or opposite direction as other shafts, so that some dimmer banks can be raised while others are lowered, the mechanism is known as "Grand Master Cross Control." Grand master cross control is a very useful feature, especially on large dimmer switchboards, and the mechanism should be constructed so that any shaft can be engaged or disengaged quickly. The smooth working of the board is also facilitated if the dimmer operating handles are fitted with self-releasing clutches.

Typical dead front type dimmer switchboards are shown in Figs. 46 and 47, and one with grand master cross control is shown in Fig. 48.

Care should be taken that quick access can be obtained to the dimmers, etc., and when space does not permit of passage room at the back of the board, this should be constructed so that access to all parts can be obtained from the front alone, and any desired dimmer or other piece of equipment withdrawn without undue difficulty. A dead front dimmer switchboard in which access to all parts is obtained from the front is shown in Fig. 46.

The circuit switches should also be grouped in much the same way as the dimmer banks, and preferably each row provided with its own master switch in addition to the grand master black-out switch. These master switches are usually known as colour masters and are controlled by the grand master switch.

It is very desirable to have " two-way and off " type circuit switches (with double the normal number of colour master and grand master switches) so that any number of switches in a row may be switched on and off by the appropriate colour master. Other switches in the same row are not then affected because they are switched in the opposite direction and governed by the other colour master switch for that row. This arrangement of switches enables black-out of a number of lighting circuits to take place while other circuits are unaffected, as might be required when the " heroine " appears to switch off the room lights, but the electric fire in the fire-place, a reading lamp, or moonbeams through the window, must remain.

It is quite usual for contactor switches operated by push button

FIG. 49. MAJOR TEN-SCENE PRE-SET SWITCHBOARD
(Reproduced by Courtesy of Major Equipment Co., Ltd.)

or control switches to be utilized for the colour master and grand master switches. Heavy loads then can be instantly handled with ease, and by mounting the contactors away from the switchboard, their operating noise can be kept from the stage.

Valuable space can often be saved by utilizing contactor switches for all the load circuits and mounting these away from the control banks of small switches, which only have to be large enough to carry the small current required by the contactor coils.

PRE-SET DIMMER SWITCHBOARDS

Intricate lighting plots are often arranged for modern stage productions, and it may be necessary to change almost instantaneously from one arrangement of the dimmers and switches to another. Sometimes difficulty is experienced in effecting the necessary lighting changes at the required speed on a standard dead front type dimmer switchboard, but, by arranging the control equipment so that lighting combinations can be pre-set in advance, this drawback can be overcome.

Pre-set boards vary considerably in design and arrangement, but one well known is the " Major " Ten-Scene Pre-Set Switchboard, which provides for the pre-selection at rehearsals of the lighting for ten scenes in advance. Each switchway is provided with a two-way rehearsal switch, a ten-scene switch, and a pilot unit. The pilot unit indicates whether the circuit is alive. The rehearsal switch is two-way and off pattern, one position giving complete control of the circuit for rehearsals or small changes, the other transferring the control to the scene switches. The switches are numbered one to ten, and by closing those that are required for a particular scene it is possible to control all the circuits for that scene on a scene master switch. Another feature of this board is that the scene master switch can be duplicated to provide complete control of the switchboard from a remote position. The dimming controls are of an orthodox pattern, with colour and scene masters. The system ensures instant changes of lighting effects by the operation of a single switch, giving a dependable one-man control. (See Fig. 49.)

Another type of pre-set switchboard is to be seen at the Empire Theatre, Leicester Square, London, where there was installed in 1928 a pre-selective switchboard capable of setting two pre-selected scenes with an independent control. (See Fig. 50.) All the dimmers are mounted at the back of the switchboard and there are separate compartments for fuses and contactors. It is also possible for this switchboard to be controlled from the centre of the stage or from any position in the auditorium by means of a trailing lead connected

FIG. 50. DIMMER SWITCHBOARD (AT EMPIRE THEATRE, LEICESTER SQUARE, LONDON) CAPABLE OF SETTING TWO PRE-SELECTED SCENES WITH AN INDEPENDENT CONTROL

(Reproduced by Courtesy of Blackburn Starling & Co., Ltd.)

FIG. 51. CONTROL PANEL MEASURING APPROXIMATELY 16 IN. SQUARE FOR CONTROLLING COMPLETE STAGE INSTALLATION BY MEANS OF ELECTRICAL REMOTE CONTROL DIMMERS

(Reproduced by Courtesy of Blackburn Starling & Co., Ltd.)

83

through a special multi-colour plug, which can be fitted into the switchboard.

Pre-set control equipment is often of the remote control type; in fact, most remote control dimmer switchboards are capable of some degree of pre-setting, as will be seen from the following pages. Electronic reactor dimmer equipment is usually arranged to provide pre-setting facilities. The Delicolor and Rollocolor control systems described later in this chapter, while not remote control apparatus in the usual sense, also provide important pre-setting facilities.

REMOTE CONTROL DIMMER SWITCHBOARDS

Cases sometimes arise when the most suitable position for the switchboard operator is not convenient for housing the whole of the control apparatus, and in these cases remote control equipment can be employed. One method is to mount the switch and fuse panels, together with the dimmer operating handles, in the required position, but to fix the actual dimmer resistance in some other part of the building, and to operate these by means of tracker wire cables or some other convenient form of link mechanism. Frequently, however, remote control is obtained by means of electrically operated dimmers and in this case a large dimmer installation can be controlled from a small and compact control panel. Furthermore, arrangement for group action and pre-setting for both switches and dimmers can be provided without much increase in the size of the control panel. (See Fig. 51.)

Another development in remote control systems is the all-electronic system which is currently available in several different designs. Essentially electronic dimming systems are comprised of certain elements. A series of small potentiometers mounted on a control desk or panel act as "pilot" dimmers on the grid control of the electronic valves. These valves may, in turn, control the current output of saturable reactors connected to the lighting load, or may themselves directly regulate the voltage of the lighting circuit. Thus, very light gauge wire between the control desk and the valve bank is sufficient. All electronic systems are extremely suitable for pre-setting. It must be remembered, however, that the electronic valves are expendable and consequently a maintenance budget must be taken into consideration.

Considerable ingenuity has been shown in the design of remote control systems and there are many different types of apparatus in existence, ranging from a control panel taking the form of a console very similar to that of a cinema organ, to a portable control desk.

AUTO-SELECTIVE CONTROL SYSTEM

Almost all remote control systems, in common with most stage dimmer switchboards, leave the lighting director or operator with

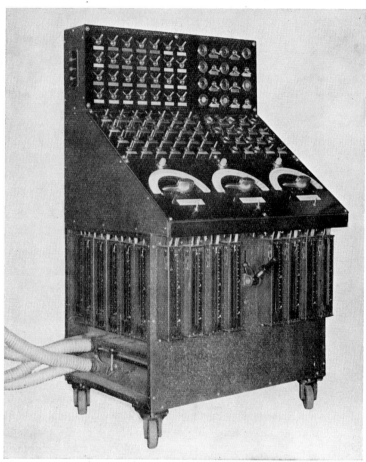

FIG. 52. CONTROL DESK INCORPORATING AUTO-SELECTIVE SYSTEM OF COLOUR MIXING (PAT.)
(*Reproduced by Courtesy of W. J. Furse & Co., Ltd.*)

the entire responsibility for the mixing of various lighting circuits to obtain different tints and effects.

One exception is the Auto-Selective Control System, which utilizes electrically operated dimmers, remotely controlled from special control dials. Each control dial bears the names of a number of colour hues and, when the selecting handle is moved to the desired colour, the dimmers electrically move to predetermined positions, to give a mixture of light that will reproduce the desired hue from the primary colours employed. (See page 3.)

FIG. 53. DELICOLOR PORTABLE CONTROL UNIT
(Reproduced by Courtesy of W. J. Furse & Co., Ltd.)

The lighting apparatus employed with the Auto-Selective System is of either the three- or four-colour type, and the control apparatus is arranged so that there is one control dial for each important set of multi-colour equipment. Thus, seven dials may be provided to control, say, the footlights, several battens, and portable multi-colour wing equipment.

Remote control apparatus frequently operates on a low voltage system, which requires only multi-core telephone cable for connection between the dimmers and the control panel. The Auto-Selective System, for example, utilizes a low voltage supply, and is particularly suitable for cinema stages, because dual control of the lighting from the stage and bioscope room adds little expense, as it is necessary only to run multi-core telephone cable from the stage control panel to the duplicate panel in the bioscope room.

Remote control apparatus can be constructed so that the switches

FIG. 53A. DELICOLOR STAGE SWITCHBOARD FOR COMPLETE CONTROL OF
A STAGE INSTALLATION
(*Reproduced by Courtesy of W. J. Furse & Co., Ltd.*)

and dimmers are controlled from a portable panel, which, by means of a flexible lead, can be moved to any desired position and even taken to the auditorium for use during lighting rehearsals.

DELICOLOR CONTROL SYSTEM

Another type of control equipment is the patented apparatus known as the Delicolor Controller. This apparatus provides all the ordinary control facilities of a dead front dimmer switchboard, and in addition enables the lighting to merge at any desired speed to a colour corresponding to any one of the general range of standard gelatine hues. The lighting changes can take place instantaneously or at the desired speed and the final colour can be adjusted at will to suit individual tastes.

Each Delicolor Control unit incorporates a dial bearing the names of approximately fifty colour mixtures, which include the standard range of stage gelatine hues, together with a number of important colours not yet available in the gelatine range.

A single Delicolor Unit is shown in Fig. 53. To cause the lighting to change, the operator has simply to move the pointer to the dial position marked with the desired colour, whereupon movement of the master change lever at the side of the unit will cause the dimmers to move to predetermined positions, giving the required colour mixture from lighting circuits controlled by the apparatus. The colours can be selected in any order and any particular hue can be reduced or brightened in intensity or dimmed right out. Thus, an operator can cause, for example, the footlights to change from Red No. 6 to Deep Amber No. 33, then to Peacock No. 15, to Lavender No. 36, and so on, simply by moving the control pointer and operating the master change lever.

The Delicolor Controller is arranged for use with four-colour lighting equipment with circuits arranged to give white, red, green, and blue light of the required hues, and the use of these circuits, either singly or together in different proportions, enables almost any known colour of light to be obtained. Thus, mixtures of white, red, and blue lighting in certain proportions will provide illumination corresponding to the gelatine filters known as Lavender No. 36.

Any colour mixture obtained from the pre-set dimmer positions can easily be varied afterwards by the operator, because the independent dimmer operating handles move with the dimmers when the change handle is manipulated; the strengths of the various circuits contributing to a colour lighting mixture are thus indicated and it is easy for the individual dimmers to be moved a little afterwards to adjust the tint.

At lighting rehearsals, the producer can nominate any colour of light he desires, simply by naming the standard gelatine colour, and he can quickly try out a number of different hues before selecting the one most suited to his purpose. Furthermore, he can improve easily on the standard gelatine range and write down lighting instructions that can be followed quickly by even an unskilled operator. Thus, if Straw No. 3 is not exactly the hue he would like,

Fig. 54. Rollocolor 4000-Watt Control Unit Providing Range of 500 Colours

(*Reproduced by Courtesy of the Color Lighting Corporation of America*)

Fig. 54a. Rollocolor Stage Switchboard

Embodying Three Control Units Complete with Intensity Controls. Grand Master Switch, etc.

(*Reproduced by Courtesy of the Color Lighting Corporation of America*)

he can dial this colour on the Delicolor Controller and afterwards modify the mixture just as he wishes.

Delicolor Control units are suitable for going on tour. A number of control units are often provided with grand master control mechanism and a number of ordinary switch and dimmer circuits included in the switchboard for the control of single lighting circuits.

ROLLOCOLOR CONTROL SYSTEM

Rollocolor is a lighting control system which resembles a radio set in appearance and is as simple to operate. The control apparatus commands lighting equipment in almost any location. It is a simple system with which anyone, even though unskilled in colour and illumination, can predetermine, select and produce over 500 hues of white and coloured light and, at the same time, determine the illumination intensity of the selected colour. The lighting equipment for use with this control system is of the 4-colour type and is available in the form of spotlights as well as floodlights, battens, footlights, etc. This system can be provided with pre-set facilities and standard control units are available to allow twenty scenes to be set up in advance and selected at will. Certain models are available whereby the illumination intensity of any selected colour of light can be increased or decreased without disturbing the tonal value of the lighting. Any selected colour of light can be modulated by hue simply by turning a single knob a little in either direction. This is very important at lighting rehearsals because the most suitable tint of light can be found out by actual experiment in a few seconds instead of accepting a certain fixed standard.

The Rollocolor system is extensively used in the United States of America. A single control unit suitable for a connected load of 4000 watts is shown in Figure 54, and it will be noticed that there is a master blackout switch on the left-hand side and four circuit breakers for the individual lighting circuits on the opposite side. This unit measures 16 in. wide, 9 in. high and 13 in. deep. A complete stage switchboard is illustrated in Figure 54A, and measures approximately 5 ft. in width. This switchboard controls all the lighting equipment including spotlights and battens for a "Theatre-in-the-Round" installation.

OTHER SPECIAL SYSTEMS

Stage lighting control apparatus is, by its very nature, a subject that allows considerable scope for ingenuity. The control systems just described by no means represent a complete list, but they are some of the best known ones in Great Britain.

CHAPTER 6

STAGE LAY-OUT AND DESIGN

LIGHTING is an integral part of stage presentation, and it is very difficult to divorce it from the factors of stage design, construction, and machinery. The stage lighting should always be considered before a stage is constructed or altered; failure to do this may result in serious errors that are afterwards difficult to eliminate.

FOOTLIGHT PROJECTION

When calculating stage sight lines it is important to remember that the footlights must project some inches above the level of the

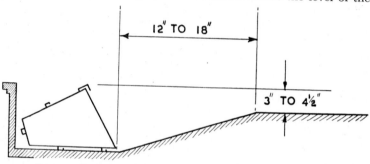

FIG. 55. FOOTLIGHT TROUGH SHOWING POSITION OF FOOTLIGHT RELATIVE TO STAGE FLOOR (SECTION)

stage floor, and this projection should be determined before all the details affecting stage sight lines are finally settled. The construction of an auditorium or stage has sometimes proceeded too far for alteration before it is realized that the projection of the footlights above stage-floor level will obstruct vision from many rows of seats.

Footlight troughs usually project some 3 in. to 4½ in. above the stage-floor level with a minimum of about 3 in. when the stage-floor is raked. It is usual to mount the footlight some 12 in. to 18 in. away from the effective edge of the stage floor, as shown in Fig. 55. No amount of ingenuity will enable a footlight to light the feet of artists when all the lighting apparatus is below the floor level. Sometimes a stage is constructed so that the footlight can be made to disappear, when desired, below floor level; as shown in Chapter 4, there are many methods of accomplishing this, but when in use, the footlights must project a few inches above the floor level.

APRON STAGES

Whenever a stage platform projects beyond the proscenium opening, care should be taken that there are adequate means of lighting people on this apron, otherwise its effectiveness will be largely nullified. It is impossible to light people frontally on an apron stage from lighting equipment accommodated behind the proscenium opening. Footlights will accomplish this purpose to some extent, but do not always give the dramatic effects required, and it is usual, therefore, to accommodate a number of spotlights or other suitable lighting apparatus at various points in the auditorium.

Spotlights mounted in or above the auditorium ceiling should be positioned to throw their light on the stage floor at an angle of not less than 20° to the vertical. Also, it is better to throw the light at an angle from either side rather than frontally, as would be the case if the spotlights were mounted near the centre of the hall. Excellent lighting results on an apron stage can often be obtained by positioning spotlights on or in the side walls of the auditorium, so that they throw light down at an oblique angle on to the stage. The actual height depends upon the width of the stage, but if the light is thrown down at the correct angle, the artists will be well covered and the light beams will not spill to any extent upon undesired areas.

Any attempt to light people on an apron stage from spotlights throwing horizontal or nearly horizontal beams of light will be marred by shadows and light spillage on to the background. If floodlights are employed instead of spotlights in any part of the hall, care should be taken to position and mask them so that the light is confined to the stage and does not illuminate adjacent areas of the auditorium.

WING SPACE

Adequate stage space at either side of the acting area is essential: without this wing space it is difficult to run stage shows without encountering many unnecessary troubles. It is surprising that so many private and even professional theatres are constructed without adequate wing space, especially when it is realized that in addition to the accommodation of stage properties, etc., room must be provided for the stage staff and artists going on and off the set.

It is held, often, that the total wing space on a stage should be equal approximately to two-thirds of the width of the proscenium opening, except in the case of small stages, when it may be necessary to have a larger ratio. This means that a stage with a proscenium opening of 32 ft. should have total wing space of 22 ft., i.e. perhaps 12 ft. at one side and 10 ft. at the other side of the stage. Many experts hold that this amount of space is not sufficient and that in professional theatres the space should be at least 16 ft. at each side.

The ideal arrangement would be to have wing space that is a little more than the width of the proscenium opening at each side of the stage. In other words, 36 ft. at each side of a proscenium opening of, say, 33 ft. Space would then be available to move box sets or wide scenic pieces sideways into the wings as required.

When planning a stage for which very little space is available, care should be taken to see that the wing space is capable of accommodating some or all of the following—

1. Part of the side flats comprising the scene.
2. Winding gear for proscenium or other curtains.
3. Stage dimmer switchboard.
4. Stage Manager's call-board and desk.
5. Lighting spots and floods.
6. Properties off stage.
7. Scenic flats, etc., not in use.
8. Fly Gallery (when stage has a grid).
9. Space to operate wall cleats, etc.
10. A piano.
11. Gear, balance-weight, and air buffer for fireproof curtains.

Space must be available, also, for the Stage Manager and his staff, the prompter, and artists leaving as well as those ready to go on to the stage. In the case of a musical or dancing show, there may be quite a number of people grouped in the wings, and, besides adequate space, care must be taken that the stage entrances are large enough for the purpose.

BACK STAGE

Some theatres are fortunate enough to have a depth of stage much greater than is likely to be used for sets, and this space can then be usefully employed for the stacking of scenic flats and properties. Some stages are provided with a scene painting dock at the back. When stage depth is restricted, however, care must be taken to see that there is room for people and even properties to pass between the scenic background and the stage wall. Although this may appear obvious, there are, nevertheless, a number of private theatres in which there is no direct access from one stage side to the other, and artists have to follow devious routes under the stage and even go out into the open when changing sides. This

93

difficulty often arises when the back wall of the stage is plastered and used as a white background for lighting effects. When this is done there must be a passage-way behind this wall directly joining the stage sides; alternatively, the rear wall must not be used for this purpose, but a dummy wall constructed in its place, at least 3 ft. in front of it. Incidentally, if there is any likelihood of the rear stage wall being used as a lighting background, care should be taken not to set any doorways in it that break the white surface or are difficult to mask from the audience.

HEADROOM

In order to fly scenic cloths, etc., intact, it is necessary for the height of a stage grid to be approximately $2\frac{1}{4}$ times the height of the effective proscenium opening. The grid itself, if possible, should be 6 ft. below the actual ceiling of the stage, with a minimum of 4 ft. The total height of a stage with a proscenium 24 ft. high would therefore be 61 ft., made up of 54 ft. to the underneath of the grid, 1 ft. for the grid thickness, and 6 ft. headroom above to the ceiling. When the grid can be so positioned, no difficulties need be experienced over the suspension of overhead lighting equipment or flying of scenic cloths, etc.

Most professional theatres have adequate headroom, but there are many concert halls and private stages in the country where this space is not available, and consequently there are no facilities for flying the scenery. Scenic canvases, however, can be flown if space a little more than half the height again of the effective proscenium opening is available, by the expedient of pulling both top and bottom of the canvas up to the grid, so that it is doubled and occupies only half its normal height. This procedure, of course, is not possible when the scenery is of a rigid nature.

Stages are frequently constructed without sufficient headroom even for the suspension of masking borders, lighting battens, etc. When the height of a stage is definitely limited, care must be taken to see that adequate space is available for these essential features. Masking borders must be deep enough to conceal lighting battens. If these are to be raised and lowered for cleaning, lamp renewals, etc., the over-all depth required will allow for lighting batten plus suspension barrel plus depth of suspension pulleys, making a total of, say, 2 ft. 6 in. The masking border will then have a depth of at least 3 ft. 3 in., to bring it 9 in. below the battens.

The number of top masking borders depends upon their depth, and if the stage ceiling is very low a greater number of borders may be necessary. These borders in turn restrict the illumination given by the lighting battens and, through cutting their angle of light, may necessitate more battens than otherwise would be needed for the stage.

FIRE SAFETY CURTAIN

Home Office Regulations stipulate that " in premises seating over 500 persons in which scenery is employed (unless they are so used occasionally and exceptionally only and not more than twelve

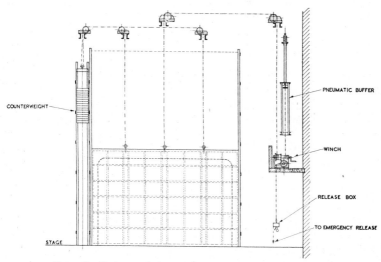

FIG. 56. GENERAL ARRANGEMENT OF FIRE SAFETY CURTAIN EQUIPMENT

days in any one year), the proscenium shall be fitted with a fire curtain. . . ."

A fire curtain usually consists of a steel framework with asbestos sheeting on the front and steel plates at the back, and has a weight of some tons. The curtain slides in vertical runners and is counterbalanced. It may be operated by hand, by electrically driven gear, or by hydraulic means.

The curtain is arranged to drop very quickly when released, so for the last two feet of the drop, air or oil buffers have to be provided that will slow down its speed and cause the curtain gently to touch the floor. The controls must be arranged so that the curtain can immediately be released from the stage manager's corner and also from some position near the stage exit door. Sometimes an additional control is provided in the auditorium.

It is usual near the top of the curtain to fit a drencher pipe

95

connected to the nearest water main, which can be turned on in the case of fire, thus keeping the curtain wet and preventing overheating or leakage of smoke. The drencher controls are hand-operated and, among other positions, are fixed adjacent to the fire curtain release handle. The drencher pipe is provided with sprinkler heads and the water pressure is raised by a booster pump, which comes into operation immediately the handle is released.

The safety curtain occupies the first 9 in. to 12 in. of space behind the proscenium opening. The proscenium curtains take up further space, so it is probably 2 ft. 6 in. to 3 ft. from the proscenium to the centre of the first lighting batten.

OVERHEAD SUSPENSION EQUIPMENT

Counterweighting mechanism is now replacing the old system of hand-operated hauling ropes; by its means heavy scenery or lighting equipment can be pulled smoothly and quickly into the flys with very little effort. Three, four, or five lines are taken from a suspension barrel (to which is attached the scene or load), over grid pulleys and main head wheels, and made fast to a balance-weight, which in turn is connected to an endless rope passing over pulleys near the floor and ceiling of the stage. By pulling this endless rope, the weight and therefore the suspension barrel (to which is attached the load) are pulled up and down.

The counterweighting framework and mechanism generally cover one of the side walls of the stage and project some 2 ft. from the wall. The balance-weight comprises a framework in which are stacked a number of removable cast-iron weights, so that the total weight can be varied quickly, to balance different loads. These loose weights are usually 56 lb. each and there are also half loads of 28 lb. These weights are piled on to the balance-weight framework from a loading platform fixed near the top of the main framework.

It is not always convenient for the counterweighting framework to cover the whole side wall of a stage, especially when there are essential doors in the wall. To avoid blocking doorways and to give more floor space, the counterweighting mechanism can be designed on a double purchase principle, whereby the scenic barrel moves 2 ft. for every foot movement of the balance-weight. The counterweighting framework then can stop short of the stage floor by some 12 ft. or more, leaving adequate space underneath for scenic flats, etc., to be propped against the wall. The spacing of counterweighted lines varies with different installations, but they can be brought together as close as 8 in. centres, so that forty-two sets of lines can be accommodated in a stage depth of 28 ft. Each set of counterweighted lines can usually take a load up to 10 cwt. but larger loads can be handled by specially constructed sets.

A lot of permanent stage lighting equipment is suspended between the scenic borders in the form of magazine battens and spot battens and, when not on counterweight lines, is suspended best on separate sets of winch lines worked from hand winches with

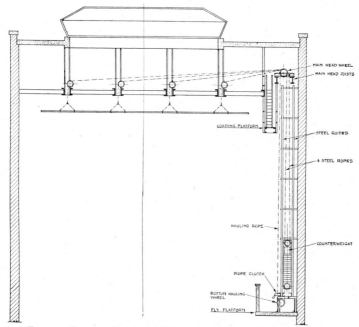

FIG. 57. DOUBLE PURCHASE COUNTERWEIGHTING SYSTEM

worm operation. It is important that the height of lighting equipment can be quickly varied and also that it can be easily lowered to the floor for cleaning, re-lamping, etc.; this is not easily done if it is suspended on hand lines only. When lighting battens, etc., can be lowered, the flexible cables feeding the apparatus have to be long enough to reach from the side of the stage to the highest and lowest positions of the equipment. The slack in these cables is usually taken up by a separate handline.

CYCLORAMA BACKGROUNDS

The word " cyclorama " is based upon the Greek word *Kyklos*, a circle, and denotes a curved surface forming the background of a stage set. In recent years, flat white backgrounds have been used to a considerable extent, but the word cyclorama continues to be applied to them, so that the word has come to imply a white background suitable for lighting effects, whether flat or curved. Actually, the word " panorama " would be more appropriate in the case of flat backgrounds.

One curved type of cyclorama comprises a cloth suspended from a curved runway; this can be taken away on a vertical roller, which runs along the track, revolving at the same time, thus winding up the cloth until it is all neatly carried on to the roller. This is necessary when the curvature of the cyclorama is of such a shape as to embrace a large portion of the stage, because when the cloth is not in use the stage wings have to be masked in a different manner. Portable cycloramas of this type demand considerable skill in the cutting and making of the cloth itself, because it is important that it hangs without creases or folds, otherwise the illusion of depth when used for sky effects, etc., is spoiled.

Cycloramas are often permanently erected in the stage and then they either have a shallow curve or are quite flat. Sometimes the structure is provided with a white plaster surface or it may take the form of a cloth stretched in a frame. One advantage of the flat type of cyclorama background is that it can be flown when the necessary stage height is available. At the Shakespeare Memorial Theatre, Stratford-on-Avon, the plaster cyclorama is suspended from a carriage moving in runners and can be moved from back to front of the stage, as required.

ROLLING AND REVOLVING STAGES

The floor of a stage is frequently constructed to include areas that are made to revolve or slide on rollers or to include actual lifts that rise from below floor level to levels higher than that of the stage floor.

Revolving type stages are now often used and are very useful for providing quick changes of scene of the box type or for scenes that employ three-dimensional set pieces. The size and the method of operation vary considerably with each installation. Sometimes lifts are built into a revolving stage so that rostrums of different heights can be arranged at will, or scenic set pieces made to appear or disappear in view of the audience, while the stage is either stationary or revolving.

A revolving stage can be fitted up on a standard stage as a temporary feature and it is not necessary to make structural alterations. These temporary revolves are hand-operated and can be constructed to go out with touring shows. The provision of a temporary revolving stage means that the height of the stage acting area is raised a little, but in most theatres this additional height can be accommodated without difficulty. Permanent installations can be of a more elaborate nature, of course, as, for example, at the London Coliseum, where the stage is provided with three separate revolving areas, i.e. Centre, Middle, and Outer, which can either move as one unit or operate independently and at different speeds in the same or different directions.

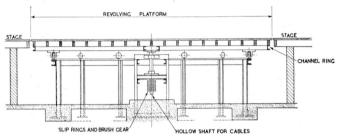

FIG. 58. SECTION THROUGH REVOLVING STAGE

Some stages are fitted with a rolling platform, which moves from front to back or from side to side of the stage area. Sometimes the rolling stage incorporates a revolving stage.

An interesting arrangement is to provide a stage with two rolling platforms that slide into the wings, one on either side, so that either they can meet in the middle or alternatively one of these platforms can fit into the full opening while the other roller stage remains in the wings. The roller stage in the wings can be fitted up with scenery while the other stage is in use in view of the audience. Actors can be seen to walk from one building or scene into another in view of the audience, if the platforms slide the sets from one side to another.

LIGHTING BRIDGES

From a lighting point of view, it is very convenient to have an overhead lighting bridge immediately behind the proscenium opening, so that spotlights and floodlights can be mounted and manipulated as desired. Unfortunately, the space required for a lighting bridge is often not available, because it is filled by many sets of lines essential for the running of the show. Certain theatres, however, are able to concede the space. A lighting bridge is particularly valuable when the stage is fitted with a cyclorama background, because special effects equipment to provide cloud effects, etc., can be located on it to great advantage.

99

It is sometimes possible to construct a theatre so that a lighting bridge is provided over the actual proscenium, but set back towards the auditorium. No space is then taken up at the back of the proscenium arch and furthermore the spotlights, etc., are better positioned to throw their light at an effective angle. The stage switchboard is sometimes positioned over the proscenium arch so that the operator has a full view of the stage action.

STAGE TERMS

Most professionals develop a language of their own and the theatre is no exception. It has, in fact, a very wide and colourful technical vocabulary. Some of the words in common use connected with stage lighting apparatus are set out below—

Act Drop. A front stage curtain which is raised and lowered.
Acting Area Lantern. A type of overhead floodlight or spotlight that concentrates light upon the acting area of the stage.
Apron Stage. That portion of the stage that projects into the auditorium beyond the proscenium arch.

Balcony Front Spotlight. A spotlight mounted on the front of the balcony.
Batten (Lighting). A lighting trough for overhead suspension.
Bay. Wing space between two adjacent pieces of scenery.
Beam Angle. The angle that contains the useful light from a spotlight, etc.
Blacklight. Ultra-violet light.
Boomerang. A vertical rod or structure usually carrying lighting equipment.
Border. An overhead masking curtain or scenic strip.
Border Lights. Overhead lighting battens.
Brace. A wooden or metal stay for propping up scenery, etc. (*See also* French Brace.)
Brail Lines. A rope used to pull into position something already suspended.
Bridge Spot. A spotlight mounted on a lighting bridge.

Centre Line. The centre rope of a set of 3 ropes.
Circle Front Spot. A spotlight mounted on the front of the auditorium circle.
Counterweighting. Raising and lowering equipment in which the weight of the load is offset by a counterbalance.
Cue Board. A control panel from which the Stage Manager gives most of his cues.
Cut Cloths. A suspended canvas scene, cut to a certain shape.
Cyclorama. A white stage background usually curved on plan, especially used for lighting effects.

Dip Plug. Lighting plug let into the stage floor.
Down Stage. Front part of stage.
Drencher Pipe. A pipe which is parallel with the top of the fire curtain and which floods it with water in an emergency.

Effects Lantern. A spotlight for use with optical effects attachments.
Entrance. A space through which artists gain access to the actual stage.

Fire Curtain. An asbestos covered framework or curtain that isolates the stage from the auditorium in the case of fire.
Flats. Pieces of scenery for masking in the stage sides.
Floats. Stage footlights.
Flood Bar. An overhead barrel carrying a number of floodlights.
Fly Gallery. The position from which stage scenes are raised and lowered.
Fly Rail. The wooden beam at the edge of the fly gallery to which suspension lines are deaded off.
Flys. The upper portion of the stage into which scenery is pulled when not in use on the stage.
Focus Lantern. Spotlight.
Footlight Well. The space in which a footlight is fixed.
Fore Stage. The projection of a stage platform beyond the proscenium arch.
French Brace. A triangular shaped brace attached to the flat which folds back against the flat when being moved and stands at right angles when set. It is often used for door-pieces etc., which need to be held firmly.
Front-of-house Spot. A spotlight on the auditorium side of the proscenium arch.
Fusible Link. A connection that melts at a high temperature, thus causing a skylight to open and create an outward draught on the stage in the case of fire.

Grid. The top stage framework from which all equipment is suspended.
Groundrow (Lighting). A portable lighting trough.
Groundrow (Scenic). A low piece of scenery standing on the stage floor.

Handline. A lifting rope operated by hand and not counterweighted.
Horizon Flood. A floodlight for the illumination of panoramas and cycloramas.
Horn Towers. A movable framework carrying loudspeaker units.
Hot Spot. A bright spot in an area of uneven illumination.
House Tabs. The proscenium curtains.

Iris Diaphragm. Spotlight attachment that controls the diameter of the front aperture.

Leg Curtain. A curtain used for masking the side of a stage.
Lighting Bridge. A bridge over the acting area on which spotlights can be mounted or suspended.
Limes. Arc spotlights used for spotting of individual artists.
Long Line. In a set of 3 or 4 ropes, the rope that is suspended farthest from the fly gallery.

Opposite Prompt (O.P. Side). Usually the right-hand side of the stage when facing the audience.

Pelmet. A curtain or decorative piece which reduces the effective height of a proscenium opening.

PERCH PLATFORM. A raised platform at the side of the stage and adjacent to the proscenium opening.

PERCH SPOT. A spotlight mounted on a perch platform.

PILOT LIGHT. Working light in a stage batten (or elsewhere).

PINPOINT. A spot beam narrowed to give a very small circle of light.

PROMPT (P. SIDE). Usually the left-hand side of the stage when facing the audience.

PROPS. Stage properties.

PROSCENIUM ARCH. The edge of the actual stage opening above the floor.

PROSCENIUM STRIP. A vertical lighting trough mounted behind the proscenium arch.

PROSCENIUM TABS. Front stage curtains.

RAKE. The slope of a stage floor from back to front.

REVOLVES. A revolving stage platform.

ROSTRUM. A wooden platform mounted on the stage.

RUNNERS. An overhead curtain track.

SAND BAG. A bag carrying about 12 lb. of sand used for weighting hand lines, etc.

SCENIC CLOTH. A painted canvas scene.

SCRIM. A coarse net cloth, partly transparent when lighted from the back.

SHORT LINE. In a set of 3 or 4 ropes, the rope that is suspended nearest to the fly gallery.

SKY BORDER. Canvas borders used for overhead masking purposes.

SKY CLOTH. A canvas background usually painted blue.

SPOT BAR. An overhead barrel carrying a number of spotlights.

SPOT LINE. A rope temporarily dropped from the stage grid for lifting purposes.

STAGE SCREW. A screw with a handle, so that it can be fixed without any tools.

TORMENTOR. A side flat or curtain adjacent to the proscenium arch.

TOWERS. Portable wooden or metal frameworks for use in the wings, on which lighting equipment is mounted for use in the wings.

TRAILER CURTAINS. Background curtains which open and close on a horizontal curtain track.

TRAPS. Hinged covers in the stage floor, giving access to dip plugs, etc.

TRICK LINE. A rope used with temporary block for lifting or swinging purposes.

TRIPE. Trailing electric cables from overhead equipment.

UP STAGE. Back part of the stage.

WEIGHT. Portable cast-iron weight for holding down braces, etc.

WINGS. Side space of a stage.

CHAPTER 7

PLANNING THE STAGE LIGHTING FOR PROFESSIONAL, PRIVATE, AND CINEMA STAGES

THE word " stage " has a very broad meaning. Many simple platforms are dignified by this title; cinemas in no way equipped for vaudeville use the same word to describe their proscenium platforms; while public halls, schools, and welfare centres employ the word " stage " in equal status with the modern professional theatre.

TYPES OF STAGES

Stages may be divided into many groups, as, for example, the following—

Professional Theatres.
Variety or Vaudeville Theatres.
Repertory Theatres.
Little Theatres.
Ciné-Variety Theatres.
Cinemas.
Municipal and Public Halls.
College and School Stages.
Temporary set-up Arrangements and Outdoor Theatres.

It is convenient, however, to divide them into six main groups, and it is proposed to consider stage lighting under the following headings—

Professional Theatres.
Variety or Vaudeville Theatres.
Repertory Theatres.
Concert and Public Halls.
Little Theatres.
Cinema Stages.

PROFESSIONAL THEATRES

Shows presented in London theatres are expected to run for a much longer period in the same theatre than would be the case in provincial cities. The stages, therefore, can be fitted up in a fairly elaborate way for each production, as the apparatus is not to be transported week by week, and the installation costs can be spread over a period. Furthermore, many of the London theatres are controlled by people who seldom put on any shows themselves. Therefore, a London theatre is usually fitted with only a moderate amount of permanent lighting equipment, but is provided with a greater number of stage plugs to which additional equipment can be connected. The extra equipment required for each show is usually obtained on a hire basis.

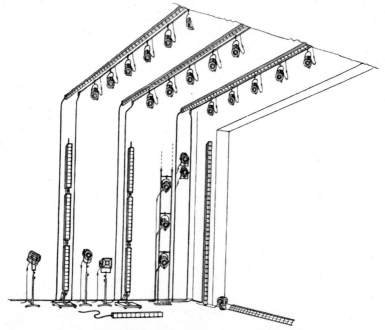

FIG. 59. DIAGRAM SHOWING SOME OF THE STAGE LIGHTING EQUIPMENT UTILIZED IN A RECENT LONDON WEST END REVUE

The provincial theatre is normally dealing with touring shows which are limited in the amount of lighting apparatus with which they can travel, and some of the provincial stages are fitted up very completely.

Almost all first-class theatre stages in Great Britain are provided with magazine compartment footlights and battens for general illumination. The overhead battens are usually suspended at 6 ft. centres, so that between four and six of them are used on a normal stage. Magazine compartment proscenium strips are usually mounted in a vertical position at either side of the stage opening. The equipment is arranged for either three- or four-colour lighting, and often the footlights (and sometimes the battens) are subdivided so that the middle and end sections can be used independently. Lamps of 150 watts are usually employed at 7 in. or 8 in. centres in the battens, lamps of 100 or 150 watts in the footlights.

Most shows to-day require at least one overhead spot batten, and in many theatres this is part of the permanent equipment. When a spot batten is permanently installed, it is usually close to No. 1 magazine batten and is often fitted with twelve spotlights for use with 1000-watt lamps. Many modern productions require two, three, or even more overhead spot (or flood) battens and acting area lanterns are used to a considerable extent on No. 2 and subsequent battens. A flood batten is often used also to illuminate the (full stage) backcloth.

Many theatres in the leading cities are provided with a number of balcony front spotlights; these are often fitted with electrically operated colour filters, controlled from the stage. Front-of-house arc spotlights also are available for the lighting from positions in the auditorium of the individual artists.

Every theatre is provided with a number of portable floodlights, and these are usually of the 1000-watt type, arranged either as single or multiple units for connection to stage dip-plugs. Some 1000-watt type portable spotlights also are available. Perch spotlights are part of the normal installation and sometimes a number of projector lamp spotlights are mounted on each perch platform. As a rule, any further portable equipment is obtained for each production on a hire basis.

The size of the dimmer control equipment varies very considerably, but even with modern dimmer switchboards, the number of dimmer ways is often not sufficient to provide all the requisite dimmer control for a particular production, and portable dimmer switchboards are then added. It is usual to control each separate spotlight or floodlight on an overhead batten by a separate dimmer and in a production these overhead units alone may necessitate the use of two or three dozen dimmers. These, together with dimmers required for footlights and battens, and additional dimmers for portable equipment, etc., make a total that usually exceeds the number of dimmer ways provided on the permanent dimmer switchboard.

A typical stage switchboard might embody seventy-six dimmer ways and ninety-one circuit switches arranged to control the lighting, as given in the Table on page 106.

In addition, switch and dimmer circuits may be provided to control some or all of the auditorium lighting. Information concerning

EQUIPMENT	DIMMERS	CIRCUIT SWITCHES
Footlights	4	4
Proscenium Troughs . . .	4	4
No. 1 Batten	4	4
No. 2 Batten	4	4
No. 3 Batten	4	4
No. 4 Batten	4	4
Perch Spotlights	4	4
Spot Batten	12	12
Acting Area Batten . . .	6	6
Circle Spotlights . . .	12	12
Stage Plugs (P. Side) . . .	8	8
Stage Plugs (O.P. Side) . .	8	8
Fly Plugs	2	2
Independent Plugs	—	4
Batten Pilots	—	4
Signals	—	1
Orchestra	—	1
Grid and Fly Lights . . .	—	2
Stage Sides	—	1
Under Stage	—	1
Board Light	—	1
	76	91

the lay-out of switches, dimmers, and master controls will be found in Chapter 5.

For touring work, it is almost routine for a portable dimmer switchboard to be provided with each spot or flood batten. Certain British theatres are provided with very elaborate permanent lighting installations, but as these are individual exceptions and not indicative of the general standard, they are not described in this book.

VARIETY OR VAUDEVILLE THEATRES

Stage lighting for a vaudeville show is usually not so elaborate as the lighting provided for a theatre production. Most of the general lighting is provided by three- or four-colour magazine compartment footlights and battens, using 100-watt or 150-watt lamps at 6 in. to 8 in. centres, while vertical side battens are usually fitted behind the proscenium arch in order to increase the intensity of the stage front lighting. Portable 1000-watt floodlights in the wings also play an important part. Perch spotlights are usually provided but powerful front-of-house spotlights are essential.

In vaudeville, the first necessity is effective and powerful illumination of the artists. Comedians, jugglers, conjurers, trapeze artists, etc., usually require powerful lighting of even intensity and free from shadows. It is also necessary to " pin-point " and " follow " two artists separately on any part of the stage. Musical and dancing acts may require artistic and dramatic lighting, and certain artists provide some spotlights or other equipment of their own to help in the creation of vivid colour lighting effects.

Full use is made of front-of-house spotlights, which are usually of the arc type, for front lighting of the artists. Balcony front spotlights are fitted in some vaudeville theatres (sometimes with remote control colour change mechanism), but are not yet in very general use. Spot battens are not yet used to any extent on the variety stage because opportunities for production lighting are not at present considered so great as with a theatre show.

Battens and footlights are usually arranged for three-colour circuits giving white, red, and blue light; when the equipment is four-colour, however, it is sometimes provided with double circuits of white instead of an actual fourth colour. On some stages, the footlights are parted in the middle to accommodate a special short trough using some 1000-watt projector type lamps, so that a powerful intensity of white light is available in the middle of the stage for additional illumination of comedians and other artists.

The dimmer switchboard must be capable of controlling all the circuits so that a series of quick changes can take place. Variety acts often call for " snap " lighting changes and sometimes two or three of these follow each other very quickly. The lighting must all be controlled by dimmers, but usually it is more a question of brightening or dimming the lights than of using production effects of the kind found in a modern theatre revue. Revues are presented, however, in vaudeville theatres, and then a certain amount of auxiliary equipment may be carried by the touring company if the show lighting is at all spectacular.

REPERTORY THEATRES

Usually the permanent lighting installation of a professional repertory theatre is quite complete, because the resident company of artists are constantly producing fresh shows, and do not wish to incur heavy production expenses, so that the lighting installation is designed to meet all normal requirements without the need of hiring additional equipment.

Often, considerable use is made of a cyclorama background, and lighting effects on it to some extent take the place of scenery. Usually, the cyclorama is of the flat or slightly curved type, and sometimes is part of the permanent set-up or structure of the stage. A portable cyclorama, however, is more valuable, because it can be varied in position and adapted more easily to the needs of various productions.

Repertory companies are often very clever in the production of dramatic lighting, and individual spotlights and floodlights are used to a considerable extent in place of battens and footlights for the general illumination of the stage. Frequently, a number of spotlights fitted with 1000-watt lamps are mounted at various positions in the auditorium, and meet most of the needs of front-of-house lighting. Stage spotlights are usually fitted with 500-watt or 1000-watt lamps. When footlights are installed, they are often constructed to disappear below stage level when not required.

The dimmer switchboard, therefore, must be capable of providing individual dimmer control of a large number of single circuits, so that the various spotlights and floodlights can be controlled as desired.

CONCERT AND PUBLIC HALLS

This heading is intended to cover all stages that are used occasionally for professional (and sometimes amateur) performances, as distinct from professional theatres in which shows are presented regularly.

The permanent lighting installation on a stage of this type is expected to provide most or all of the required lighting effects, because the production usually will not allow of much expenditure on the hire of additional lighting equipment. Therefore, the permanent lighting installations are often of a very efficient nature; for the factors of durability, current consumption, and maintenance are all carefully considered in the first place, whereas in the case of a professional theatre production the consumption of electricity is of less importance than the cost of the equipment, owing to the relatively short life of a show. The lighting installation in a Hall has also to be capable of meeting very varied demands, because the stage may be used for every variety of purpose.

Both footlights and overhead lighting battens are usually of the magazine compartment type, employing 100-watt or 150-watt lamps. In modern installations they are generally arranged for four-colour lighting, giving circuits of the three primary colours, red, green, and blue, with an additional circuit of white light. Often the footlights are of a " disappearing " type, so that the platform may be used for non-theatrical purposes. The distance between battens is not so standardized as in the case of the professional theatre, but is dependent upon the individual arrangement of top borders: usually the battens are spaced at centres of between 6 ft. and 9 ft.

The general lighting of the stage is provided by the footlights and battens, but the illumination of the acting area is often intensified by light from projector lamp spotlights mounted in the auditorium. Usually, front-of-house spotlights are not employed to " follow " the artists but rather to build up an adequate intensity of illumination so that an artist is well lighted when standing on any main part of the stage. The auditorium spotlights are often mounted in the ceiling void and project their light on to the stage through traps in the ceiling. Sometimes they are mounted on the side walls of the auditorium and occasionally on the balcony front. These spotlights vary in size according to the needs of the stage, and 500-watt or 1000-watt lamps are usually employed, although 2000-watt lamps are sometimes used, especially when the spotlights are mounted in the ceiling void. Changes of colour filter can be provided by fitting a spotlight with electrically operated colour filter mechanisms controlled from the stage.

Considerable use is made of portable wing equipment, and often this is of the multi-colour type, so that colour mixing effects can be provided. A number of individual spotlights and floodlights are often accommodated in the front part of the stage, either at the sides or overhead, and sometimes a batten is divided into sections with a spotlight between each pair of adjacent lengths. When perch spotlights are employed, they are usually left in a fixed position and not employed to " follow " artists.

Many stages are provided with a flat or nearly flat permanent cyclorama background. Many of the people concerned with production in private theatres are keenly interested in the art of drama, and frequently use the lighting in a more daring manner than is normal with professional productions. An illuminated cyclorama background can be made also to reduce the expenditure on scenery.

The cyclorama backgrounds are usually lighted at the top by one or two rows of magazine compartment lighting battens, or alternatively, by a flood batten. The bottom lighting is usually obtained from removable groundrows of the magazine compartment type, connected to dip-plugs. Excellent results can often be obtained by using two rows of overhead batten with 150-watt lamps at 7 in. or 8 in. centres or by an equivalent wattage in a flood batten. The groundrows generally employ 100- or 150-watt lamps at 7 in. or 8 in. centres. A higher wattage is provided usually for the blue circuit.

The permanent and often slightly elaborate nature of the lighting installation requires a stage dimmer switchboard of a very complete type, and many stages are fully provided with advanced control equipment. The installation often has to be manipulated by relatively inexperienced operators and the dimmer switchboard must be able to give the required control without too much ingenuity on the part of the operator. The need for good control equipment is emphasized further by the fact that artistic and dramatic lighting effects may be attempted on a somewhat high level, and the time available for lighting rehearsals may be even less than is the case with professional theatre shows.

Each individual colour circuit in the footlights and battens requires to have separate dimmer control, and if there is a cyclorama background then each colour circuit in the equipment that illuminates it requires also a separate dimmer. Auditorium and any other spotlights giving widely different angles of lighting require to have separate dimmer controls. Multi-colour and other wing equipment on either side of the stage means that at least four dimmers are required for each side. Finally, one or two spare dimmer circuits should be provided for occasional use.

Each lighting circuit should be controlled by a circuit switch, preferably of the two-way and off type, one side of which is controlled by the grand master black-out switch. The other side may be connected to a second master switch or left connected on the main supply to the board. In this manner, a number of circuits can be controlled or left unaffected by a black-out, when it is not desired to black-out all lighting on the stage simultaneously. Colour master switches also are desirable.

The dimmers should certainly be arranged for group action, and it should be possible to lock any desired number to the master shafting for collective operation.

The total load involved in the lighting installation will almost certainly require a balanced supply (unless the main electricity supply is two-wire), and then a dead front type board is necessary. A typical arrangement of switches and dimmers for such a board is given in the Table on page 111.

Because of the desire to provide artistic and advanced stage lighting effects from equipment that must be manipulated by people who are often without much switchboard experience, many of the larger halls have a more expensive type of control equipment than is found in many professional theatres. The Auto-Selective and Delicolor Control Systems, for example, are found in many concert halls and large private theatres, as they are particularly useful for operation by semi-skilled or unskilled switchboard operators.

	SWITCHES	DIMMERS
Footlights: 4 colours . . .	4	4
No. 1 Batten: 4 colours . . .	4	4
No. 2 Batten: 4 colours . . .	4	4
Cyclorama top lighting . . .	4	4
Cyclorama bottom lighting . .	4	4
Multi-colour P. Dips . . .	4	4
Multi-colour O.P. Dips . . .	4	4
Spare Plugs	2	2
Auditorium Spotlights . . .	3	3
Perch Spotlights	2	2
Pilot Lights	1	—
Board Light	1	—
	37	35

LITTLE THEATRES

The foregoing remarks apply mainly to the larger and more elaborate types of stage found, for example, in many municipal concert halls and welfare theatres, but they also apply to a number of school stages and private halls. There are, however, a large number of less pretentious stages in halls and schools, where the lighting installation is, of necessity, of a more simple nature: these are briefly discussed in the following paragraphs.

Footlights are usually considered to be the most important single piece of lighting equipment in a modest installation, and, in so far as they certainly flood the entire stage with light, this opinion is probably correct. Certainly, footlights by themselves are much more effective than a single overhead lighting batten, especially if they are mounted a little in front of the proscenium arch, so that actors are not on top of them. If the only lighting comes from an overhead batten, harsh face shadows appear when the artists are near the front of the stage.

There is a school of thought, however, which holds that the first fundamental of stage lighting is directional lighting on to the acting area. This can be achieved quite simply by mounting a spotlight at both sides of the hall so that the beams overlap on the main part of the stage. If the spotlights are of the prismatic lens plate type, they provide a soft-edged beam of light that is so variable in width that it is possible to cover most of the stage acting area with them if required. By control of each spotlight on a separate dimmer, the intensity from either spotlight can be varied so that a " modelling " effect is achieved on objects and people. This effect may be further enhanced by the use of filters of different colours in the two spotlights.

While two spotlights will thus cover the acting area, additional lighting is required to " fill in ", and to soften shadows. This can be done by also using footlights and/or overhead battens. Many advocates of directional lighting do not care for the use of footlights because of the indiscriminate floodlighting they provide, and prefer overhead battens for the desired general illumination. The number of battens required depends largely upon the lay-out of the stage borders, for although one batten may be sufficient if suspended on a clear stage, the near presence of a masking border will cut off the light at an angle and another batten will be required to illuminate the darkened area behind it.

An alternative method is to supplement the two auditorium spotlights by additional spotlights (and/or floodlights) in the stage wings, and to dispense with battens and footlights altogether. Thus, another soft-edged spotlight in the front wing at each side of the stage, plus a floodlight at each side near the back, will probably give sufficient extra illumination for a stage of moderate depth, and will open up very interesting possibilities in directional lighting. The two floodlights should give a wide angle distribution of light so that between them the whole of the backcloth can be lighted. The two auditorium spotlights, plus the two front stage spotlights, should adequately cover the whole of the acting area; if each is controlled by a separate dimmer, very fine dramatic effects of light and shade can be achieved. Furthermore, delightful effects can be obtained from " modelling " with colour-tinted lights.

The two auditorium spotlights should be mounted well up from the floor, so that the light is thrown downwards towards the stage. They can be mounted on the side wall, but sometimes there is a roof truss or convenient beam across the ceiling that can serve as a suspension point. It is important that the spotlights are widely separated so that on plan their light is thrown on to the stage at an angle. Prismatic lensplate spotlights employing 500- to 1000-watt gas-filled projector lamps give good results; the larger size is recommended because front-stage illumination should be fairly powerful in order to hold its own with lighting from the stage spotlights and floodlights. If plano-convex lens spotlights are utilized, it may be necessary to fit a white frosted gelatine in front of the lens to diffuse the light and soften the edge of the beam.

The two spotlights in the front stage wings can be mounted on floor stands or brackets well above the heads of people standing in the wings, or it may be more convenient to suspend these spotlights from above. 500-watt lamps will give good results if used in 10 in. diameter prismatic lensplate spotlights. The two wing flood units should each be mounted on a telescopic floor-stand and fitted with a 500-watt gas-filled lamp.

This arrangement has been described in detail because it is an inexpensive method of achieving good stage lighting based on sound principles. Excellent dramatic effects can be obtained and the factors of light, shade, and colour contrast employed with effect. The electrical installation cost is low because there are only six pieces of equipment to be connected and the dimmer switchboard is simple, requiring a maximum of six dimmers. Furthermore, additional lighting equipment, as, for example, footlights, can be added at a later date, without spoiling in any way the original scheme.

Reverting to battens and footlights, it may be said that adequate stage lighting can be obtained by their use alone, and the majority of small stages in this country are lighted in this manner. This method certainly does provide even, shadowless illumination, and if the only requirement is to flood the stage with light, battens and footlights will achieve this result. They do not, however, afford much opportunity for dramatic lighting, because directional effect is limited, and each piece of equipment floods the stage with light. The footlight should be three or four feet shorter than the width of the proscenium opening, and the front batten should be nearly equal to this width. The other battens may require to be a little shorter than the first batten, as it is usual to reduce the width of the set towards the back of the stage.

Whenever possible, battens and footlights should be of the magazine compartment type, that is with a separate compartment and reflector for each lamp bulb and with a colour filter in front of the clear lamp when coloured light is required. These compartments should be wired on four circuits for white, red, green, and blue light; but if installation expense must be kept to a minimum, they can be wired on three circuits for either white, red, and blue colours, or yellow, pink, and pale blue.

The open type trough employing coloured lamps is a cheaper arrangement and, as far as white light is concerned, gives fairly good results as a footlight. The intensity of coloured light provided by varnished or colour-sprayed lamps is much lower, however, than that obtained from clear gas-filled lamps behind gelatine or other filters in the magazine compartment type equipment. Footlight troughs, with compartments at 8 in. centres, and fitted with 100-watt lamps, give excellent results for most small stages, although it is advisable to fit 150-watt lamps behind blue colour filters. When electricity consumption must be kept to a minimum, 60-watt lamps can be used, with 100-watt lamps behind the blue filters.

Magazine compartment battens are much more effective for both white and coloured light than open type troughs from overhead positions, because the light has to be concentrated in a downward direction and the open type trough exercises very little control over the light given by the bulbs. Compartments at 8 in. centres, fitted with lamps of the same size as the footlights, give excellent results. At least two battens are recommended, but the exact number depends upon the depth of the stage and the lay-out of overhead masking borders.

Two or more spotlights mounted in the auditorium greatly increase the dramatic possibilities of the stage lighting; if this is not convenient, a spotlight at each side of the front part of the stage improves the effects. If the footlights and battens provide a fairly good intensity of illumination, the auditorium spotlights should preferably employ 1000-watt lamp bulbs, and the stage spotlights 500-watt or 1000-watt bulbs. It is very convenient also to have one or two portable wing floods on the stage, so that backings to doors and windows may be illuminated.

The stage dimmer switchboard is always rather a problem with modest installations, because the fundamental requirements of a lighting plot are apt to be the same whether the stage is large or small. Certainly, each separate lighting circuit requires its own circuit switch, and there should be also a master black-out switch. Means should be provided, however, to enable certain circuits to be left " alive " (as desired) when the black-out switch is operated, so that black-out of most of the lights in a set may take place still leaving, say, an electric fire alive or moonlight shining through the window.

The number of dimmers is largely a matter of expenditure and the professional requirement of one dimmer per circuit is often not feasible. If the dimmers are to be reduced to a minimum, arrangements should be made for the footlight circuits to be independently dimmed from the batten circuits. Thus, four-colour footlights and three four-colour battens can be controlled on eight dimmers by grouping the same colour circuit in the three battens together on one dimmer. There should be at least one dimmer for floor plugs at each side of the stage, so that a dimming effect can be worked independently from either side. If there are spotlights in the auditorium mounted close to each other, these can be collectively dimmed; but if the spotlights are lighting the stage at widely different angles—for example, from opposite side walls—then each spotlight should be on a separate dimmer. Perch spotlights, i.e. front stage spotlights in the stage wings, should be controlled also on a separate dimmer at each side.

These requirements really represent the minimum that will give effective control of stage lighting. An installation comprising four-colour footlights, two four-colour battens, two auditorium spot-lights, and portable stage equipment, would then involve the follow-ing dimmers—

Footlights	.	.	4 switches	.	.	4 dimmers
Battens	.	.	8 switches	.	.	4 dimmers
Auditorium Spotlights	.	2 switches	.	.	2 dimmers
Stage Dip Plugs	.	.	4 switches	.	.	2 dimmers
			18			12

CINEMA STAGES

Almost all cinema stages now are provided with colour lighting equipment, which will illuminate the cinema screen and curtains, so that film titles, etc., can be flooded with colour. Some stages are equipped also for variety acts and even stage productions.

Cinema stage draperies and screens can be illuminated effectively by means of footlights and overhead battens of the magazine com-partment type, employing 100-watt or 150-watt lamps at 7 in. or 8 in. centres. It is usual to arrange for 100-watt lamps in the red and green circuits, with 150-watt lamps behind the blue filters. If a stage is not used for acting purposes, the footlight and battens should be arranged for three-colour lighting with red, green, and blue colour filters, so that almost every variety of colour hue may be produced by using these circuits either singly or together in different proportions. When stage acts or productions are presented, the equipment should be wired on four circuits, so that a circuit of white is available in addition to these three colours.

The footlight should be a little shorter than the width of the proscenium opening. The first lighting batten should be of approxi-mately the same length or perhaps a little longer, but any other battens will probably be shorter in length owing to the decreasing width of the stage setting. The number of battens depends upon the lay-out of the top masking borders and the depth of the stage, but with non-acting stages one or two overhead battens are usually employed. When the cinema screen is quite close to the footlights and is provided with screen curtains, only one overhead lighting batten is necessary, provided there is not a border coming between

115

it and the screen curtains in such a manner as to cut off the light at an angle that will leave the upper part of the curtains in shadow.

The cinema screen and stage draperies can often be lighted quite effectively from footlights alone, but while adequate illumination may thus be provided, there is an absence of coloured contrast lighting. Overhead lighting battens are employed, therefore, in addition to footlights, so that the stage curtains and cinema screen can be lighted in different colours at top and bottom (see also Chapter 14).

The beauty of effect on stage curtains and draperies is amplified if, in addition to top and bottom lighting, the curtains also are floodlighted at both sides. This side lighting catches the folds of the curtains in a different manner, and if the side lighting is in correct colour contrast to the top and bottom lighting, some very beautiful effects are possible. The side colour lighting is usually obtained from three-colour troughs or wing flood trolley units.

The proscenium curtains are usually illuminated by the stage footlights alone. When these are only a short distance away, it is important that the lighting distribution should prevent undue " blobbiness " and should allow a good colour mixing from the different circuits on a reasonable area of the curtain.

Each colour circuit in the footlight and battens requires to be controlled by a separate dimmer, so that the colours may be blended together in different proportions and the illumination brightened or dimmed as required. Multi-colour wing equipment also requires separate dimmers, but on non-acting stages it is usual for the wing equipment on both sides of the stage to be controlled on the same set of dimmers. Sometimes, two overhead lighting battens also are grouped on the same dimmers. This is quite a good arrangement, provided the battens are not likely to be used separately to any extent. Thus, six or nine dimmers will frequently provide adequate control of cinema stage colour lighting for the draperies and screen.

These dimmers are usually controlled from the bioscope room, so that the operator can manipulate the lights to synchronize with the opening and closing of the curtains, etc. If the dimmer controls are situated on the stage, an operator has to go there in order to work the stage lighting. While this arrangement is sometimes justified when the lighting installation is an elaborate one used mainly for stage shows, it involves unwarranted labour and trouble when the lighting is employed only for cinema screen and curtain effects. In the case of more elaborate stage lighting installations controlled by a stage dimmer switchboard, it is usual to provide dual control of footlights, and perhaps one or two sets of batten circuits from the bioscope room.

Curtain backgrounds in a stage production must be lighted in line with the general colour scheme and purpose of the scene; but apart from stage presentations, cinema curtains and draperies can be vividly colour lighted for their own effect. Beautiful and striking colour lighting effects can thus be employed, and, if intelligently chosen and used, can be of considerable value in presenting the various items of a film programme in an attractive manner. The striking appearance of these curtain and screen colour effects increases the need for *artistic* colour combinations. Since the permutations and combinations on a curtain lighted from, say, three or four different directions are very great, special automatic control equipment is often employed instead of hand-operated dimmers. This control equipment causes the stage colour circuits to be blended so that a large range of resultant hues can be obtained from each set of lighting equipment, and the colour mixtures themselves can be contrasted with artistic effect. The operator is thus relieved of the work and responsibility of providing these colour harmonies and, apart from starting and stopping the lighting, is free to attend to his many other duties. The Auto-selective Control System, for example, is used in many cinemas, and by simply turning the pointer on a dial to the required colour combination, the operator ensures that the stage lighting automatically merges into this effect, and, if desired, continues changing into subsequent colour combinations until the lights have to be dimmed.

One advantage of automatic lighting control systems is that they can usually be controlled from dual positions, i.e. from the stage and from the operating box, without much additional expense.

Many cinema stages, however, are fitted out to allow for the presentation of stage shows, and in these cases a stage lighting installation is usually of a more elaborate nature. Colour lighting effects are required for the curtains and screen, but in addition lighting facilities for a stage production must be available. Many ciné-variety theatres are provided with very fine stage lighting arrangements, in some cases among the best in the country. Cinema stages arranged for the presentation of single acts or simple displays, however, require little in addition to the ordinary battens and footlights, other than front stage lighting from spotlights in the bioscope room. The battens and footlights should have a fourth circuit of white, and the front-of-house spotlight arrangements should be adequate to cover a number of people on the stage at one time.

Some stages, however, are fitted to allow for special settings, obtained by either draperies or scenic cloths, and often the stage grid is sufficiently high to allow for the screen, etc., to be flown. Stage presentations can then be provided with settings that rely to a considerable extent on colour lighting for their effect. Lighting is provided from the wings as well as from battens and footlights, and the striking appearance of the colour lighting makes it essential that the acting area can at the same time be lighted in more normal colours. Spotlights employing projector lamps are required for this purpose and some of these can be accommodated on the stage. Additional spotlights are often accommodated in convenient positions in the auditorium, as, for example, in a ceiling cove or behind ceiling traps.

These spotlights build up the illumination intensity of the acting area but do not " follow " individual artists, as this effect is usually provided by arc spotlights located in the bioscope room. In large ciné-variety theatres, however, there is sometimes a special spotlight chamber, much nearer to the stage than the bioscope room, in which operators are accommodated with powerful arc spotlights. This spotlight chamber is usually mounted in the auditorium ceiling void.

Productions presented in a ciné-variety theatre rely to a considerable extent on the permanent stage draperies and lighting equipment for their settings, and it is not usual to budget for heavy expenditure on special scenery or for hire of additional lighting apparatus. The permanent lighting installation, therefore, is quite complete, and is intended to allow for a wide range of effects, so that new settings can be created from stock draperies over a fair period of time.

The variety and ease of lighting changes is dependent upon the dimmer control system, and some very fine sets of control equipment are to be found in ciné-variety theatres. In fact, the spectacular nature of these presentations has considerably influenced the design of stage lighting control apparatus. There are so many types in use as to make the control of ciné-variety stage lighting a subject of its own, but information concerning some of the types available will be found in Chapter 5.

Dimmer control equipment mounted in the bioscope room must be of the dead front type, so that there is no possibility of sparks or flames escaping into it. The usual practice is to mount a dead front dimmer switchboard flush in one wall of the bioscope room, but with the actual dimmers and fuses, etc., housed in the adjacent room. Only the switches and dimmer operating handles are then in the bioscope room, and are usually connected by toggle links, through slots in the panel, to dimmers accommodated in the adjacent room.

PART III. THE ART OF STAGE LIGHTING

■

CHAPTER 8

DIRECTIONAL LIGHTING, SHADOW, AND COLOUR FOR FACE AND FIGURE

THE form of an object is decided (visually) by the direction of the lighting in relation to the eye of the beholder. When the direction of light is nearly the same as the line of vision, shadows are less perceptible and the image appears even. As the angle between the direction of light and the line of vision increases, the shadow component becomes more emphatic and there is greater contrast. The appearance of form depends entirely upon contrasting values of light.

VISUAL PERCEPTION

It is commonly believed that objects and people have a fixed appearance and that illumination is necessary only to dispel darkness and to cause this appearance to be seen. This is not the case, however, because, as shown in Chapter 1, visually we are conscious only of an image of light formed by light rays reflected from the object in question; when a change in the direction or colour of the lighting alters the reflection of light rays in the direction of the beholder, there is a change in the appearance of the object.

The appearance of people and objects on the stage is a very important matter; considerable pains are taken in many ways to present those aspects that have the right dramatic values. In general, it has not yet been realized to any extent that the actual appearance of any object depends entirely upon lighting direction, contrast, and colour, and that, since the theatre stage allows for concealed lighting from almost every direction and in any colour, a very potent technique is available for those who understand how to use it. Light not only affects, but determines, the appearance of all things on the stage.

Line, plane, mass or volume, contour, texture, light and shade, and colour are the main elements of visual composition. These visual elements can be perceived by the eye only as elements of light, and a little consideration based on the facts briefly outlined in Chapter 1 shows this to be the case.

An example of the way in which light determines the apparent form of an object is shown in Figs. 60, 61, and 62. Again, when coloured light is used to illuminate an object of a different colour hue, there is a change in that object's appearance; an example of this is shown in Plate III.

When dealing with any aspect of Art it is always difficult to give exact rules, and in the case of so vast a subject as the appearance of objects and people it is unwise to be dogmatic. However, certain fundamental facts must be understood if one is to have a reasonable grasp of the subject. Their application, however, is a very individual matter, and should be left to the intelligent interpretation of the person concerned. Particularly is this true of stage lighting and the part it plays in dramatic art.

DIRECTION OF LIGHT

With light derived from a single source, if its direction is nearly the same as the line of vision, the illumination is even; but as the angle between them widens, contrast increases and the effect becomes more dramatic. When the light falls on an object at an angle of 45° to the line of vision, a fairly normal appearance is usually achieved; but as the angle increases, the shadow component becomes more conspicuous, and as it approaches 90° the contrast effect becomes very marked. When the direction of light is at more than right angles to the line of vision, the shadow area becomes greater; and as the angle widens towards 180°, the lighted area decreases, until at 180° the object is either in complete silhouette or rim-lighted only, according to the relative sizes of the light source and the object.

The angle between the direction of light and the line of vision can vary on both horizontal and vertical planes, and the appearance of an object depends upon just how the light is located. Thus, an angle of 45° on a horizontal plane may give quite a different effect to that given by the same angle on a vertical plane. This will be apparent from illustrations given in Figs. 60, 61, and 62.

With the lighting of people, it is useful to consider directional lighting in the form of zones. On both horizontal and vertical planes, a simple rule to follow with a single light source is as follows—

Angle of 0°–30° to line of vision	. .	Even shadowless lighting.
Angle of 30°–60° to line of vision	. .	Normal lighting.
Angle of 60°–90° to line of vision	. .	Contrast lighting of great dramatic value.
Angle of 90°–130° to line of vision	. .	Acute angle lighting from the rear.
Angle of 130°–180° to line of vision	. .	Rim lighting reduced to silhouette.

There is one amendment to this grouping: i.e. when the direction of the light comes from a point below the line of vision and the angle between the line of vision and the direction of light exceeds 45°, dramatic rather than normal effects on the face are provided.

For general stage purposes, a very good angle of light from a single source is 45° to the angle of vision, with the light coming

FIG. 60. MASK LIGHTED FROM SIDE BY SINGLE LAMP ON
HORIZONTAL PLANE
Angle of incidence: 45°.

down at an angle of 45° to the horizontal. This is a pleasing arrangement on most people; but if, by any chance, it is necessary to soften unwanted shadows, this angle should be reduced in either or both directions. Thus, for elderly or for very thin people, the lighting should be of a frontal nature. Men and women with normal faces usually look well under 45° angle lighting, but sometimes fat people are flattered by a greater angle, say, 60° or 70°. A rugged appearance can often be imparted to men by sharp angle lighting, say, 70° to the angle of vision. Ladies usually look their best with a more normal angle, say, 45°.

FIG. 61. MASK LIGHTED FROM OVERHEAD BY SINGLE LAMP
Angle of incidence: 45° above horizontal.

Several men and women are frequently seen on the stage at one time, and while it is often not feasible to arrange the lighting so that it is adjusted to each separate character, it is possible for the producer to arrange that the dominant character or characters are lighted in the most effective manner and that their appearance is dramatically correct.

Most of the stage lighting equipment is located behind the

proscenium opening; from here it is not possible to use spotlights at an angle of, say, 45° to the horizontal line of vision from the auditorium, unless the artist keeps well back stage. This difficulty can be overcome by locating additional spotlights at the sides of

FIG. 62. MASK LIGHTED FROM UNDERNEATH BY SINGLE LAMP
Angle of incidence: 75° below horizontal.

the auditorium, so that 45° angle lighting is provided when an artist comes to the front of the stage.

Generally, it is more convenient to suspend stage lighting equipment overhead rather than in the stage wings, partly because of the necessity of keeping the side entrances as free as possible from obstruction, and partly because there is more utilizable space overhead. The tendency, therefore, is to use more overhead spotlights

123

than wing spotlights. This means that most of the spot lighting on to the acting area is coming down at an angle from above, and side lighting on the horizontal plane can be achieved only by wing equipment. Perch spotlights give side lighting at a relatively gentle angle, however, and as they are located near the front of the stage, can do very useful work over a large part of the acting area.

LIGHTING COMPOSITION

It has been assumed earlier in this chapter that the stage lighting comes from one direction only, whereas, in practice, this is the case only in exceptional circumstances. Lighting is usually provided from many different directions to build up pleasing, as well as practical, illumination. Care is taken to ensure that characters and objects are properly visible from all parts of the auditorium, but emphasis is given to lighting from certain directions.

Stage lighting should be built up into a composition in much the same way as a picture is composed or a building designed on sound architectural principles. The lighting composition should be intelligently constructed and based on understood principles; the final results should be satisfying from an æsthetic as well as from a practical point of view.

The final stage lighting composition may be built up of a number of other lighting compositions, each one complete in itself. Thus, there may be one composition for the lighting of the artists (including minor compositions for the principal characters), and another lighting composition for the illumination of the setting. As a general rule, the lighting for the characters and the lighting for the setting should be somewhat complementary to each other, the latter being subordinate to the former.

The remainder of this chapter is concerned mainly with the lighting of people on the stage, although some of the principles enumerated can be applied also to the lighting of settings.

Apart from special effect lighting, the author considers that most lighting compositions should be constructed on the basis of certain main factors: (a) Dominant Lighting, (b) Secondary Lighting, (c) Rim Lighting, and (d) Fill-in Lighting. The factor of Rim Lighting cannot always be utilized, but when possible and desirable can add considerable effect to a lighting composition.

The lighting composition must be logically constructed and the Dominant Lighting should set the dramatic key of the scheme. It must be clear and straightforward in nature and must have clearly pronounced direction, intensity, and colour.

The Secondary Lighting is supplementary to the Dominant

Lighting and may be rather more complex in nature, comprising lighting of various intensities and colours from different directions. This lighting should bring the idea suggested by the Dominant Lighting nearly to completion.

Rim Lighting is achieved by high intensity lighting from a position behind the object, so that only certain edges are illuminated. The effect is usually obtained from a spotlight, and the intensity of the Rim Lighting generally should be higher than the rest of the lighting employed, so that high-lights are created.

The Fill-in Lighting is more in the nature of relatively low intensity floodlighting, but it may vary to some extent in colour and intensity from different directions. This lighting brings the ideas suggested by the Dominant Lighting to completion, and imparts a smooth effect to the whole composition.

DOMINANT LIGHTING

When building up a lighting composition, attention should be paid first to the Dominant Lighting, since this sets the key-note and determines the dramatic values of the whole scheme. Starting from this point, the Secondary, Rim, and Fill-in Lighting may be developed logically, since they are subordinate to the intention of the Dominant Lighting and, in fact, bring out the values it is intended to express. This procedure may be likened to constructing first the bones of a body (Dominant Lighting), then covering with flesh (Secondary Lighting), finally, adding charm to its appearance (Rim Lighting and Fill-in Lighting).

The direction of light is discussed earlier in this chapter, and the effect achieved from Dominant Lighting at certain angles is shown. The Dominant Lighting in most stage shows comes from a position well to the front of a character. It is not generally realized that lighting of considerable dramatic value can sometimes be achieved when the Dominant Lighting comes a little behind, rather than in front of, a person on the stage.

The Dominant Lighting increases in dramatic effect as the angle between the line of vision and direction of lighting increases. There is considerably more dramatic effect when the Dominant Lighting is, say, at right angles to the line of vision, than when it is of a more frontal nature. Acute angle lighting tends to provide an emotional effect also. Dominant Lighting that is at an angle of less than 45° to the line of vision gives smooth, " soft " lighting, while Dominant Lighting that comes a little behind the character creates a very vivid effect.

It will be appreciated that the " line of vision " must be

125

considered only as an average for the whole audience, and that it is impossible accurately to take this into account for every individual person present.

Dominant Lighting can accentuate the beauty of a lighting composition quite apart from its dramatic value and, conversely, it can create a dramatic effect that is hard and ugly. Strong dramatic effect is not required always, but this does not indicate that Dominant Lighting should not be of an acute angle type, as the latter may help to build up a lighting composition of considerable beauty and appeal.

Dramatic effect generally requires a fairly marked contrast between the intensities of the Dominant and the Secondary Lighting, and usually the effect increases as the contrast deepens. The presence of shadow and areas of low intensity lighting tend to suggest dramatic or emotional issues and the more these shadows or low tones predominate, the greater their effect. As the angle between the line of vision and the direction of the Dominant Lighting increases, this lighting covers less of the face and figure of a character, and so increases the area of shadow and low intensity illumination. The contrast effect can be softened by increasing the intensity of the Secondary Lighting, and when this is done the dramatic effect may be reduced but the beauty accentuated.

When the Dominant and Secondary Lighting are fairly close to each other in intensity, a pleasing, balanced effect is generally obtained, and this type of lighting is very suitable for comedy and other scenes that do not require dramatic emphasis.

Sometimes beauty of effect must be subordinated entirely to the necessity for high intensity shadowless lighting, which enables an audience to perceive exactly what a character is doing, as, for example, a conjurer or juggler. Many vaudeville acts require lighting of this nature, and in these cases the Dominant Lighting should be nearly parallel with the line of vision. Alternatively, Dominant Lighting may not be required at all, and instead the character or scene is flooded with high intensity lighting from many directions so that shadow effects are almost nullified.

Front-of-house spotlights are excellent for Dominant Lighting of a frontal nature. While they can be used to pinpoint or flood various characters, it should be possible to employ them so that angle lighting from spotlights on the stage (or spotlights in the auditorium situated for angle lighting) can be utilized to provide the actual dominant intensity.

While the Dominant Lighting must generally appear to come from one direction, it is often necessary to employ a number of lighting units to achieve this result. The stage characters move about, and it is almost impossible with only one piece of lighting equipment so to cover the whole of the acting area that the lighting always appears to fall at the same angle. If it is desired to light the main character from the actor's right at a certain angle, it may be necessary to use, say, a spotlight plus end spotlights on two or more spot battens, together with spotlights mounted at the side of the auditorium.

In order to get a clearly defined direction of light, the illumination should be provided by apparatus with a fairly concentrated area of light source, for example, a spotlight or floodlight. Battens and footlights are really not suitable, because, while they do give directional lighting in one plane, the length of the equipment and number of lamps employed provide general floodlighting on the other plane. The footlight, for example, will floodlight evenly a person standing in the middle of the acting area, and an overhead batten will do the same, providing the character stands well back from it. In other words, battens and footlights are very useful for general floodlighting, but can be used for directional effect only in a very limited manner. Multi-colour wing flood equipment or compact sets of overhead multi-colour flood equipment, in practice, serve quite successfully as directional lighting units.

SECONDARY LIGHTING

The amount of shadow created by the Dominant Lighting is determined by the Secondary Lighting; as this approaches the former in intensity, the contrast effect becomes less. Secondary Lighting, therefore, helps to determine the degree of dramatic effect created by the Dominant Lighting. Furthermore, it is used to create balance and build up beauty of composition.

While the Secondary Lighting is subordinate to the Dominant Lighting, it is somewhat complementary to it. Thus, if the Dominant Lighting is clearly defined in direction and intensity, the Secondary Lighting may be built up with a soft merging of light of varying intensity and from several directions. These directions will be determined by the degree of contrast and amount of shadow or half-tone required.

The lighting composition is brought to completion by the Fill-in Lighting, so it is not necessary to build up the Secondary Lighting to achieve this final effect. As the Fill-in Lighting will ultimately soften the contrasts, the Secondary Lighting may be composed so that there is still a clearly defined contrast, even when soft glamorous lighting is required.

The Secondary Lighting can be fully complementary to the Dominant Lighting in the sense that it is almost the exact opposite, except in intensity. Alternatively, Secondary Lighting in itself may resemble the Dominant Lighting: i.e. it can have a clearly

FIG. 63. AN EXAMPLE OF RIM LIGHTING

marked direction and illuminate from a wide angle to the line of vision.

RIM LIGHTING

The pictorial effect of a lighting composition can often be enhanced by the addition of Rim Lighting. The degree of high-lighting achieved depends on the angle of the lighting to the line of vision, and on its intensity relative to the rest of the lighting. The light source must be situated well behind the person or object, or else too large an area will be illuminated; usually, the best effects are obtained when the lighting unit is located at an angle of between 120° and 150° to the line of vision on a horizontal plane. An example of Rim Lighting will be seen in Fig. 63.

In theory, equally good Rim Lighting can be achieved from a light source at an angle of 120°–150° to the line of vision, but on the vertical plane, so that the light is thrown on to the back of the object from above. In practice, however, this is somewhat difficult to arrange, because the masking borders are generally in close proximity to the lighting equipment, and then it is difficult to throw the light towards the front of the stage without obstruction. However, excellent results can be achieved by suitable spotlights located in the stage wings, so that generally there is no need to make special arrangements for locating the Rim Lighting units overhead.

This back lighting must usually have a higher intensity than the rest of the lighting employed in the composition, or the effect of high-lighting will be more or less absent. The dramatic effect is emphasized when the Rim Lighting is very powerful, because of the increased contrast between illumination intensities.

In addition to the attractive " edge " effect, Rim Lighting imparts high-lights to the hair, and when the lighting intensity is sufficiently high it can light up loosely arranged hair so that it tends to glow in a most charming manner.

Rim Lighting adds beauty of effect, but this is not always required. Furthermore, the contrast in illumination intensities is sometimes undesirable, especially in the case of certain vaudeville acts, when shadowless, even illumination is the fundamental requirement.

FILL-IN LIGHTING

Contrasting areas of illumination can be brought nearer to the same intensity by soft floodlighting, which reduces the amount of contrast. Fill-in Lighting achieves this effect, and moreover, finally softens shadows created by the Dominant and Secondary Lighting.

Directional stage lighting is rarely confined to white light, and usually there is a contrast between the colours of the Dominant and the Secondary Lighting. This colour contrast can be softened by delicate general lighting of another colour, which, by blending with both of the stronger colour lighted areas, brings them more into unison with each other. The Fill-in Lighting should be applied after the Dominant and Secondary Lighting have been settled.

The footlights are excellent for this purpose. They not only illuminate almost every object and person on the stage, but project their light from a direction opposite to that of the rest of the stage equipment, and thus are well placed to soften shadows. The intensity of the Fill-in Lighting, however, should be kept down to a point where it softens, but does not obliterate, the effect built up by the Dominant and Secondary Lighting.

Footlights are often controlled so that the middle and end sections can be used independently. When this arrangement is available, different colours can be employed in these sections with great effect. Generally speaking, these colours should not be in sharp contrast with each other, but should in themselves present a soft gradation in hue from one section of the footlight to another. Often it is very effective to have in the middle section a colour contrasting with another tint in both end sections.

Overhead battens and any kind of equipment that will provide fairly general floodlighting can be used to build up the final effect provided by the Fill-in Lighting. Sometimes it is effective to use the battens each in a different colour, so that they provide a soft gradation in colour hue from front to back of the stage.

When high intensity Dominant and Secondary Lighting is employed, and so directed that little of it falls upon the scenic setting, the Fill-in Lighting can often be used with a strong enough intensity to provide general lighting of the actual setting. When this arrangement is possible, a very pleasing effect can be obtained, as the acting area is then lighted to a much higher intensity than the rest of the stage.

SHADOWS

Shadowless, even lighting is the last thing desired on the stage when an artistic illumination effect is required. Occasions arise when it is important for a character or object, or even a scene, to be illuminated without shadow, as, for example, when trapeze artists are performing, but on these occasions it is not artistic effect that is primarily required, but rather, high intensity general illumination.

The *art* of stage lighting depends on the clever use of shadow and of contrasting areas of brightness and colour. There is all the difference in the world between controlled shadow and unwanted shadow.

Form depends for its appearance upon gradations and variations of colour and illumination intensity. It is shown in Chapter 1 that colour is an element of light, so the last statement really means that form depends for its appearance on gradations and variations of light. When illumination gradually diminishes over an area, the darker portion is often referred to as being in shadow, and in this sense shadow is very important for the definition of form.

There is another type of shadow, however, which really is a true shadow: i.e. the shadow cast by an object through its obstruction of light. While this cast shadow does not determine the appearance of the object itself, it nevertheless can play an important part in the dramatic value of a lighting composition, though care must be taken that an effect is not spoilt by the presence of unwanted cast shadows.

One drawback to the strong frontal lighting of characters from spotlights mounted on the centre of a circle front is that cast

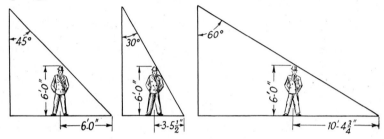

FIG. 64. VARIATION IN LENGTH OF SHADOW ACCORDING TO ANGLE OF LIGHT

shadows are formed on the background and can be obliterated only by lighting the actual background to a relatively high intensity, which in turn may upset the balance of the lighting composition.

It is better to use spotlights at an angle that will keep the cast shadows on the floor. A rule to remember in this respect is that when a spotlight beam falls on an object at 45°, the cast shadow is of the same length as the height of the object, and this length decreases as the angle of lighting becomes steeper, and increases as the angle of lighting approaches the horizontal.

Cast shadows are hard and clearly defined when the source of light is small (e.g. a standard spotlight lens), and are softer, with blurred edges, when the source of light is relatively large (e.g. a 1000-watt floodlight). A shadow tends to become sharper as the distance between an object and the background diminishes.

Front-of-house spotlights for "pin-pointing" artists on the stage should, whenever possible, be located so that cast shadows are thrown on to the floor and not, as sometimes happens, right on to a back-cloth behind the person. When such a spotlight is located badly, the cast shadow is sometimes so clearly defined on the scenery as to be almost more interesting to the eye than the actual character, which, of course, is bad showmanship. When two such spotlights

131

are employed, perhaps in different colours, the result is two shadows, each varying in colour, and here again there is considerable distraction from the artist. It is very difficult, of course, to avoid part of the cast shadow spilling on to a back-cloth suspended very near to the actor, and care should be taken to provide a reasonable distance between them.

Shadows can have dramatic value, as, for example, the grotesque shadow of a murderer seen on a wall. Distortion of a normal shadow can often be used to suggest the presence of evil and sometimes a horror effect is achieved by showing only the shadow of a person. Conversely, shadows can have an æsthetic value, which, either alone or in conjunction with the general lighting composition, adds to the pictorial beauty and significance of a scene.

BACKGROUND LIGHTING

Brightness is very much a relative matter, and an object on a stage appears to be well or badly lighted according to the ratio of its illumination to that of its surroundings. One candle brought into a darkened room gives brightness, but an object illuminated to an intensity of 10 f.c. appears poorly lighted against a background of 100 f.c. It is essential, therefore, that the most important objects on the stage should be those that are illuminated most effectively, so that the attention of the audience is naturally drawn to them.

Generally, this means that the artists should be lighted more powerfully than their surroundings. It must be remembered, also, that the size of a person compared to that of the scenic background is small, and to off-set the general effect of the illuminated set it is necessary to provide a much higher illumination intensity on the characters. Again, people on the stage rarely exceed 6 ft. in height, whereas the scene itself may be 20 ft. high, and it is often desirable for the lighting on the latter to diminish towards the top so that emphasis is given to the lower parts of the scene adjacent to the acting area.

It is important that the appearance of a background should not be spoilt by the presence of unwanted cast shadows from artists or objects, and the stage lighting should be directed to prevent this happening.

Impressive results can sometimes be obtained by showing the artists in semi-silhouette against the surroundings. Furthermore, there are occasions when people can be shown in pure silhouette against the background, and when this is dramatically possible very striking effects can be achieved. For pure silhouette effects it is necessary to confine the background lighting to an area well behind the person or object concerned, and not to let lighting from the sides fall upon him or it, or the pure silhouette will be lost.

The background lighting can comprise a lighting composition in itself and, together with lighting compositions for the characters, can be embodied in a final arrangement of pictorial completeness, presenting the right dramatic values for the purpose in question.

COLOUR OF THE LIGHT

So far, this chapter has been mainly concerned with the direction of lighting, but the final values are dependent upon the colour of the light also. The dramatic effect achieved by any one arrangement of lighting can be varied tremendously by changes in the colour of light employed from different directions. Often, in fact, the dramatic effect can be completely reversed.

It is most important, therefore, to consider the use of coloured light, so that tints may be chosen to fit in correctly with the directional values of the lighting and also to achieve the required dramatic effect. Accordingly, the following chapter is devoted to the subject of Colour Harmony, Contrast, and Discord, in order that a basis may be established for the selection and grouping of coloured light. Application of the principles of directional light and colour are further discussed in their practical utilization for stage lighting in Chapter 10.

CHAPTER 9

COLOURED LIGHT, ITS HARMONY, CONTRASTS, AND DISCORD

IT is shown in Chapter 1 that, while red, yellow, and blue are the primary colours for pigments and dyes, the primary colours of light are red, green, and blue. The former are known as subtractive primary colours and, while generally named red, yellow, and blue, would be more exactly described as magenta, yellow, and blue-green. Mixtures of coloured light are based upon the additive method of colour mixing, and the primary colours of red, green, and blue give secondary colours of magenta, yellow, and blue-green.

PRIMARY COLOURS IN LIGHTING

The primary colours for mixtures of coloured light are therefore the opposite to the primaries employed for the mixing of dyes and paints. Very little has yet been published on the subject of colour harmony for areas of coloured light. Almost all the textbooks on the subject of colour harmony deal with the colours obtained by the subtractive method, i.e. by mixtures of dyes, paints, etc. While the additive and subtractive methods of colour mixing are opposite to each other, the subject of colour harmony, contrast, and discord is concerned with the arrangement of the colour hues produced, and not with the method of providing these tones. To a certain extent, therefore, we can base our knowledge of the relationships of areas of light upon experience gained in the harmonizing of paints, etc.

Coloured light possesses a luminosity not available in dyes and pigments. Moreover, different colours can be blended into each other with an effect quite different from that produced with paints, because of the additive effect achieved. It would be incorrect to apply exactly the rules of colour harmony, contrast, and discord as already developed for pigments to the art of colour lighting, but these rules can act as a guide and serve a useful purpose until the knowledge of the use of coloured light has developed sufficiently to enable a separate set of rules to be built up.

COMPLEMENTARY COLOURS

Chromatic colours can be either fully saturated pure colours or pastel tints or neutral tones of these pure colours, as shown in Chapter 1.

Since pastel and neutral colours always are derivations of

pure colours, it is convenient to illustrate certain relationships between them by locating the main colours around the outside of a circle.

The colour circles vary a little according to different schools of thought, but in the main are all quite similar. Two examples are given in Figs. 65 and 66, and it will be seen that while there is, in fact, a difference between Rood's circle and the colours as arranged

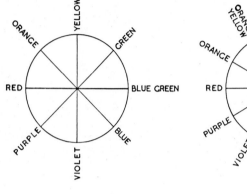

FIG. 65. COLOUR CIRCLE ACCORDING   FIG. 66. COLOUR CIRCLE ACCORDING
      TO LUCKIESH   TO ROOD

by Luckiesh, the differences are not very great. The Luckiesh circle is, however, based upon an analysis of wave-lengths of coloured light, and is another representation of the facts illustrated by Maxwell's colour triangle in Fig. 2. There is sometimes a little confusion over the exact meaning of the terms " blue " and " violet," but throughout this book the term " blue " is employed to signify a spectral blue, and the term " violet " for blue with a little red added to it.

Complementary colours will be found at opposite ends of a straight line drawn through the centre of a diagrammatic colour circle, and it will be seen in Fig. 65 that green and purple, blue and orange, red and blue-green, etc., are pairs of complementary colours.

When, in dealing with coloured light, we speak of complementary colours we mean those that, when superimposed, produce white light.

Another arrangement of colours is seen in the colour circle (after Titchener) shown in Fig. 67. The complementary colours shown in this diagram are different from those shown on the Luckiesh circle (and, in fact, from those on most colour circles) and are based upon a certain idea of colour vision. In practice, however, the writer finds that the complementary colours based upon this arrangement are pleasing and very satisfying when applied to areas of coloured light, though he does not necessarily accept the theory of colour vision involved.

The complementary colours shown in Fig. 67 are very pleasing when seen side by side, whereas areas of complementary coloured

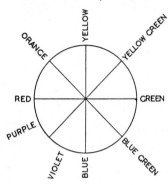

FIG. 67. COLOUR CIRCLE BASED ON TITCHENER'S THEORY

light based on the Luckiesh and Rood circles are in some cases pleasing but in other instances rather discordant. For example, orange-yellow and blue present a pleasing combination, whereas red and blue-green make rather a harsh contrast. On the other hand, the arrangement of colours in Fig. 67 shows yellow and blue as a pair of complementary colours, but in the case of red gives green as the complementary colour. Areas of red and green light of spectral purity look very pleasing side by side. The complementary colour of blue-green is given in Fig. 67 as orange, which is a much more pleasing combination than red and blue-green (Fig. 65).

COLOUR HARMONY

According to Barrett Carpenter,* the three great principles of colour are harmony, contrast, and discord. He bases his rules on Rood's natural order of colour, and defines simple harmony as the effect of using any colour with its next neighbour or neighbours in their "natural order." In considering contrasting colours we are concerned with the relationship of hues that are quite different from each other, while discords are the effect of a reversal of the natural order of colour.

Rood's natural order of colour is very interesting and is based upon observations of colour in nature. It is deduced that yellow is the lightest colour and violet the deepest, and that, starting from yellow, there are two colour routes to violet, with the colours deepening as they approach violet. One route is yellow, via yellow-orange, orange, red, magenta, purple, to violet; the other route, yellow,

* *Colour*, by H. Barrett Carpenter.

via yellow-green, green, peacock blue, turquoise, cyan-blue, to violet. In other words, one route progresses from yellow to violet via red, giving one series of colour tones, and the other route via green, giving a different series of colours.

According to Rood's natural order of colour, any pair or trio of colours adjacent to each other, on either path, are in harmony when the lower colour is deeper than the one immediately above it. Thus, yellow and orange harmonize when the orange is a little deeper than the yellow. Red and magenta harmonize when the magenta is the deeper of the two. Again, green and green-blue are in harmony when the green-blue is the deeper colour, since it is the lower one, i.e. nearer to violet.

The writer has experimented with the relationships of colour-lighted areas based on this rule, and finds that the results are very pleasing and that Rood's law can be taken as a definite guide to harmony when dealing with colour lighting.

Harmony of colour can thus be created by taking two colours closely related to each other from Rood's colour circle (Fig. 66) and arranging these so that the colour nearest to violet is deeper than the one nearest to yellow. A trio of colours can be arranged on the same basis, the middle colour being deeper than the colour nearest to yellow and lighter than the one nearest to violet. Arrangements of this kind provide a simple scheme of colour harmony.

More elaborate schemes of harmony can be created by arranging a composition in which a pair or trio of harmonizing colours are supported by lighter or darker sets of the same colour.

COLOUR CONTRASTS

Complementary colours are true contrasts and when placed side by side tend to intensify each other. Contrasting colours are, however, not always complementary colours.

Contrasting colours that are truly complementary to each other will be found at the ends of a straight line taken through the centre of one of the colour circles illustrated. As has already been pointed out, some of these pairs make rather a harsh contrast when seen side by side. A more pleasing effect is obtained when the contrast to a given colour is spread into two or three colours, the centre or centre colour of which is a true complementary of the first-named colour. Thus, instead of blue-green as a contrast to red, green and cyan-blue colours, as a pair, are more pleasing. Alternatively, red can be effectively contrasted by a trio of colours, green, blue-green, and blue.

Effective combinations of contrasting colours can be obtained by selecting three or more colours located at equal intervals round the periphery of a colour circle. Thus, on the basis of Rood's circle, orange-yellow, green-blue, and violet make an attractive trio. Again, green, ultra-marine, and orange go well together.

It is most important that contrasting colours that are intended to be balanced with each other should be kept on the same level of tone, i.e. should have the same degree of saturation.

Contrasting colours that are not complementary colours tend to change their appearance when placed side by side, and this is particularly true when the area of one colour is greater than that of the other. The reasons for this tendency are briefly discussed in Chapter 1, under the headings " After Images " and " Simultaneous Contrast." The high luminosity of colour-lighted areas increases the tendency of non-complementary but contrasting colours to change the appearance of each other.

When it is desired that contrasting colours shall harmonize, they can, with effect, be arranged in accordance with Rood's natural order of colour, i.e. the colour nearest to violet should be deeper than the one nearest to yellow.

DISCORDS

The use of a colour in opposition to the rules that provide harmony will create discord, and one example is the reversal of Rood's natural order of colour. A small amount of discord, however, can be made to complete a colour composition. It is an interesting fact that while large masses of discordant colour are most unpleasant, a small touch of discord in a composition seems to bring it to completeness and give it a sharpness that it would otherwise lack.

An example of discord would be the use of pale violet in a composition comprising orange and the contrast blue and green-blue. A touch of this discordant colour, however, can be used with good effect. Of course, if employed to any large degree, it will upset the balance of the composition.

TONE AND ITS EFFECT UPON COLOUR SCHEMES

It has been shown in Chapter 1 that the fundamental factors of any colour are Hue, Brightness (value or brilliance), and Saturation (chroma). When dealing with coloured light, the term saturation indicates the amount of white light in the colour. A fully saturated colour has no element of white, but as the percentage of white light increases, so a colour is said to become less saturated. Therefore, saturation concerns the tone of a colour and is described by Webster as " that attribute in respect to which colours may be differentiated as being higher or lower in the degree of vividness of hue."

Generally it is important to keep the main colours in a balanced composition on the same tone level. Tone contrast can, of course, be employed, but the contrast can often be slight in the case of large areas of colour, though it may be more marked when dealing with small quantities.

Colours can be employed so that the tone level is kept constant by the use of adjacent colours; thus, the effect of shade is produced by colour variations rather than by loss of brightness. A column lighted on one side by yellow light can therefore be illuminated from an acute angle on the other side with orange light, so that an appearance of shade is achieved by the gradation of yellow into orange.

One of the difficulties experienced in stage lighting is that the standard range of gelatine colour filters is made up of colours that vary very considerably in their degree of saturation. This means that sharp tone contrasts are introduced when they are not required and considerably limit the effective use of many combinations and contrasts. For example, there is a considerable difference in the degree of saturation of Straw No. 3, Amber No. 4, and Orange No. 5 gelatines, and were this not the case it would be possible to use these three colours in proximity to each other with very great effect, because they would then represent differences of hue on the same tone level.

This difference in degree of saturation can, of course, be overcome by using three- or four-colour lighting equipment, and mixing the primary colours in different proportions to achieve the desired hue, because it is then possible to provide light of different colours from various sets of equipment and to build them up so that colour hues are on the same tone level. The writer finds that it is much easier to build up attractive colour harmony and contrast effects by using multi-colour equipment in this manner, than by the employment of gelatine filters. The problems of dimmer operation, etc., which are then introduced, can be almost entirely overcome by the use of suitable control equipment, as for example, the Rollocolor Controller described on page 90.

COLOUR COMPOSITIONS

Monochromatic colour lighting has very little colour value, because without a standard of comparison it is difficult to locate and appreciate a colour hue. As soon as a comparison colour is introduced, the factors of relative intensity and area arise, and then we are at the beginning of a colour composition. Almost all arrangements of stage lighting, therefore, should be lighting compositions, because there is rarely any justification for monochromatic or flat white lighting.

The complete stage lighting of a scene may be a compound composition in the sense that it is made up of a number of minor compositions built into one master arrangement. Thus, there may be one lighting composition for the main acting area with minor compositions for lighting of characters on other parts of the stage, and another composition for the lighting of the setting—the whole lighting being blended together so as to make one final composition, which is balanced, dramatically correct, and satisfying.

Frequently, the lighting of a character should in itself be a colour lighting composition, as, for example, when a singer is the centre of interest, or is alone on the stage. Again, there may be a curtain background to the artist which is lighted from several directions, and here too the lighting should be a complete composition in itself, but conceived in the right relationship to the lighting composition for the artist.

CHAPTER 10

BUILDING UP A LIGHTING COMPOSITION

THE planning of stage lighting must be thought of in terms of an artistic composition, but certain practical considerations have to be kept in mind.

THE LIGHTING OF AN ARTIST

Consideration should first be given to the purpose for which the artist appears on the stage. The lighting should bring out this purpose and determine the appearance of the artist and setting, at the same time providing the required standard of illumination. If the artist is a conjurer, a high intensity of shadowless illumination may be required, but if he is a criminal creeping across a darkened room, then heavy shadows and low intensity lighting may be the aim.

The relationship of the artist to the setting should also be considered, as many types of dramatic effect are possible according to their relative dominance. Sometimes more dramatic emphasis can be given to a character on the stage by a pure silhouette effect than by the lighting of the character to a much higher intensity than the surroundings. On other occasions, it may be necessary to avoid any form of distraction and to focus attention on the artist by high intensity lighting with very subdued illumination on the setting.

Acting area lighting may be required for a single artist (as in the case of a vaudeville act), or for numbers of people (as, for example, in the production scene of a revue), or for various characters in a play. It is obvious that a different treatment is required in each case, and it is equally clear that hard and fast rules for the lighting are impossible. Certain features, however, can be considered, and it is hoped that the following comments will be of interest.

LIGHTING OF THE VAUDEVILLE AND
CONCERT ARTIST

Artists in a variety act or concert appearance may be presented in a pleasing setting, but probably this will have no direct connection with the entertainment, as might be the case in the presentation of a play. The setting is therefore completely subordinate to the entertainment and must usually help to focus attention on to the artist. Any type of background or lighting that distracts attention from the artist must therefore be avoided. This does not mean that interesting and attractive settings must not be used, but implies that they must be in harmony with the entertainment and help to hold the attention of the audience to the whole act, of which, of course, the artist is the focal point. Thus, a stage setting lighted with bluish shades of light would help to support and focus attention on an artist spotlighted in yellow light.

A normal stage setting is much larger in area than a human being, and it is natural for the eye to rove over the background unless the artist is *doing* something that holds the attention. The audience is more likely to watch attentively a dancer than a singer. Lighting can be used to counteract this difference in area and to give due importance to the artist by the correct use of brightness, contrast, and colour.

The artist should be lighted to a much higher intensity than the surroundings. If sombre clothes are worn, an even greater brightness ratio will be necessary, as only the face, hands, etc., of the person can appear brightly lighted. Thus, a very high ratio of illumination is required when the artist is a man in evening dress and the background is a drop-cloth painted in very light colours. Assuming that the person is lighted by spotlights at maximum intensity, it may be necessary to lower the brightness of the foot-lights, battens, etc., which illuminate the background, until the desired contrast ratio is achieved. This may have the effect of reducing the general brightness of the stage as a whole, but it will certainly help to focus attention on the artist.

The colour of the lighting is also very important, and here again contrast can play an important part. Excellent results can always be obtained by the use of colours that are in harmony somewhat in accordance with Rood's Law, and the brighter, paler colour should generally be focused on the artist. Thus, pale yellow from the spotlights on a stage flooded with orange light, or pink on a stage flooded with bluish light, will give pleasing results. Again, striking results will be achieved by using colours that are in contrast, i.e. yellow light against a blue lighted background, or pink light against a background flooded with pale green.

As the area of the setting is so much greater than the size of the artist, very good results can sometimes be obtained by lighting the person in a tint that is actually a discord to the colour used for the lighting of the scene. This at once focuses attention on the artist and actually can create a very pleasing arrangement, because, as already pointed out, a harmonious colour composition seems to be sharpened and brought to completeness by a small amount of colour discord. A singer flooded with pale pink light could be presented in a setting flooded in deep blue and green light. The discord should always take the form of a much paler colour on the artist than would be justified in normal colour calculations. In other words, colour harmonies or contrasts can be chosen, but with the stage colours fairly saturated in hue, with the lighting on the artist very de-saturated. Since pink is a very de-saturated red or mauve hue, harmonizing colours to this basic hue would be orange or deep mauve, while the complementary colour would be green or green-blue. By the use of these saturated colours for the setting, and the de-saturated colour (i.e. pink) for the artist, a discord is created because of the difference in saturation values; but, owing to the relatively small area of the discord, the results are usually very effective.

Usually it is better to employ two or three different colours for the lighting of the setting in order to avoid a monotonous effect. A good rule to follow, when the setting permits, is to use lighting of two or three closely related colours from different directions, with a certain amount of colour contrast splashed on at a suitable point. For instance, yellow and red light could be used from two directions with a splash of greenish-blue contrast provided by a flood or spotlight. The artist could then be lighted with very pale lavender light.

Certain types of entertainment are best presented under white light, and this applies particularly to comedy acts. Experience has shown that high intensity white lighting often creates a better environment than colour-tinted lighting when laughs are required. White spotlighting also is very effective when the stage is flooded with coloured light for a more artistic effect, and will always show the artist in strong relief. From the point of view of the artist, however, white spotlighting tends to be rather too harsh, and it is usual to use slightly colour-tinted light to soften the effect.

When an artiste is wearing a long gown and is standing fairly still, pleasing effects can often be obtained by lighting the lower portion in a colour from one spotlight, with another spotlight superimposed so as to light the head and shoulders, etc. In this way, a bluish light, say, can be projected on to the dress, while a pale pink light is superimposed for the lighting of the head and arms, etc.

Sometimes colourful, rather than natural, lighting is required, as, perhaps, in the case of a contortionist or dancer. Vivid colour effects can then be obtained by lighting from widely different angles in contrasting colours. The front-of-house spotlights must then be supplemented by additional spotlights or floodlights on the stage in order to get the required angle lighting. Very striking colour effects are possible, and the artiste can be shown up sharply by the correct use of colour lighting on the set, so that the factor of colour contrast, as well as the ratio of lighting intensity, helps to make the person the focal point of the whole presentation.

LIGHTING OF THE ARTIST IN THEATRE PRODUCTIONS

The vaudeville or concert artist usually appears in a setting that has no association with a story or a sequence of events. The setting for a play, however, may contribute to the story and impart important information concerning the characters; consequently, it may be necessary to regulate the lighting of the setting to provide continuity of effect, even though a solo artist may be holding the stage with entertainment that normally would be supported by lighting of quite a different nature.

In musical comedy and pantomime, usually no attempt is made to provide continuity of effect in a scene, but with artistic licence the lighting of the setting is changed just as frequently as desired, in order to provide suitably lighted environments for different numbers. Particularly in revue, deliberate attempts are often made to change the appearance of the setting completely by alterations in the lighting, so that new and different aspects of the setting are constantly unfolded to the audience.

When the illumination of the setting can be changed at will for any desired effect, the lighting for a solo artist can be built up on the lines already suggested for a vaudeville or concert act. It is possible that lighting of a more elaborate nature may be employed, because more intricate lighting plots are often utilized for musical comedy and revue productions. Thus, in addition to light from front-of-house spotlights, the artist may be picked out by spotlights or acting area floods from an overhead batten, and by further spotlights on the perches and in the wings. Delicate shading in colour is then possible and delightful colour compositions can be built up. Salmon light from a front-of-house spotlight, supplemented by white light from an overhead spotlight or acting area flood, with yellow light from front-stage wing spotlights and medium blue light from wing spotlights for the back-stage, for example, will give a very delightful effect.

It is difficult to impart the best appearances to a person by evenly flooding him in light from all directions. Instead, there should be modulations of intensity in order that contour can be emphasized. Furthermore, when artistic effect is required, there can be variations in the colour as well as the intensity of the lighting. Barrett Carpenter points out that " it is a well-known principle in flesh painting ' to keep your shadows warm and your lights cool.' Thus, cold highlights on warm yellows or reds, and delicate cool grey or bluish edges of half tones supply the slight but necessary discords." Although this advice concerns painting, the principle is sound when applied to lighting. The Dominant high-light can be a whiter colour than the Secondary Lighting, so that the low intensity areas are lighted in a warmer colour. Rim Lighting, from spotlights or floods partly behind the artist, can be made to give, say, a bluish tinge to the edges.

Attractive colour lighting compositions on an artiste can often be built up by the use of Dominant Lighting at an angle in, for example, very pale yellow, superimposed upon Secondary Lighting that illuminates in warm yellow on the same side but farther behind the person, linked with contrast lighting (not complementary) on the opposite side, perhaps in mauve. The Dominant Lighting will smooth out these richer colours of the Secondary Lighting, except where low intensity or shadow areas are created, thus giving the effect of softly coloured shadows. The picture may be rounded off by the use of the footlight in blue-green to give Fill-in Lighting with bluish-green under-shadows, while a touch of Rim Lighting from the back in a suitable colour will complete the effect, making a very charming picture.

A rather more vivid and colourful effect can be achieved by the use of Secondary Lighting illuminating opposite sides of a person in complementary colours. One of these complementary colours should be a colour similar to the Dominant Lighting but more saturated, as, for example, yellow, when the Dominant Lighting is pale gold. The Fill-in Lighting can then be of a colour half-way (on a colour circle) between these complementary colours so that an effect approaching white light is achieved where lighting from all three directions is superimposed. When the Dominant Lighting is applied at a front angle, the secondary colour nearest in hue to the Dominant Light should be on the side more brightly lighted by the latter, so that an effect of shading in colour is achieved on one side, with the light changing to an edging of complementary colour on the opposite side. Under-shadows will tend to take on the hue of the Fill-in Lighting, providing a pleasant but gentle contrast to the colours of any side shadows.

When an effect of realism is required, it may be necessary to provide an excuse for the use of coloured light from various directions. This is not difficult when it is remembered that in nature the light reflected from trees, grass, flowers, etc., is all colour-tinted, and even the light from the sky (not the sun) is usually bluish in colour. Standing in a field near a red brick wall that faced the sun that was nearing the horizon in a blue sky, one would be lighted with a Dominant Light of pale gold from the sun, with reddish tinted light on the opposite side reflected by the wall, and greenish tinted light from the grass in the field. Bluish light from overhead would also be provided by the sky. Thus, in actual practice, people are often lighted in delicate or even deeply coloured light from various directions due to reflection of light from coloured surfaces.

On these lines, lighting may be used to suggest the colour of surfaces not actually seen by the audience. Outdoor scenes often include no attempt to produce the appearance of grass, etc., on the stage floor, but additional effect can be given to the whole scene if lighting from the footlights is pale green in colour, as though the upward light were reflected from a grass lawn or field.

Sometimes vivid and startling colour effects are required rather than a balanced artistic colour composition. Sharp colour contrasts will always be obtained if light of complementary colours is projected from opposite directions. As will be seen from Figs. 65, 66, and 67, pairs of complementary colours include orange and blue, green and purple, red and green-blue. The sharp contrast effect from the use of light of complementary colours from opposite directions can always be modified by projecting a certain amount of white or near-white light from an intermediate angle. The strength of the white light will determine the amount of colour seen by the audience and it will be found that quite a small amount of white light will considerably soften the colour contrast effect. The effect is often improved by the use of one of the complementary colours in a higher intensity than the other. Furthermore, an improved modelling effect may be achieved if one of the complementary coloured lights is a little more to the front of the person than the other.

When a person is to be lighted in a pronounced colour tint, additional effect can usually be achieved by a Dominant front light of the desired colour and then lighting from each side in separate colours corresponding to the fundamental colours comprising the Dominant Lighting. Thus, if the main lighting is yellow, the fundamental colours are red and green, and if these are projected from opposite sides of the stage, a very delightful effect is achieved. Again, if the Dominant Light from the front is moonlight blue, the fundamental colours of blue and green can be used separately from each side of the stage. One result of this arrangement is the deepening

146

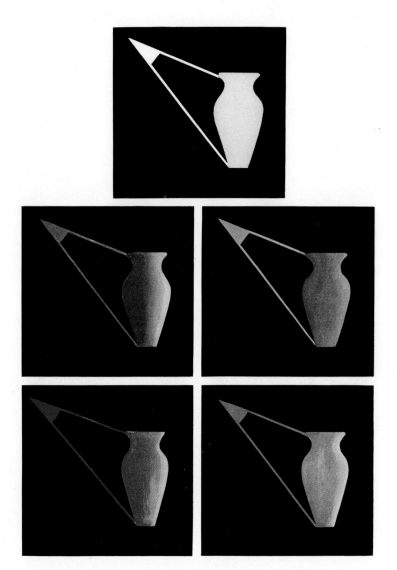

PLATE III

APPEARANCE OF YELLOW VASE WHEN ILLUMINATED BY LIGHTS
OF DIFFERENT COLOURS

of colour of the light at the sides of the person; although there is a variance in colour on either side, both these hues are derivatives of the Dominant Light and so enhance its value.

It is important to keep balanced colours in a lighting composition at the same degree of saturation, and one of the difficulties encountered with the use of standard theatre gelatine filters is the varying

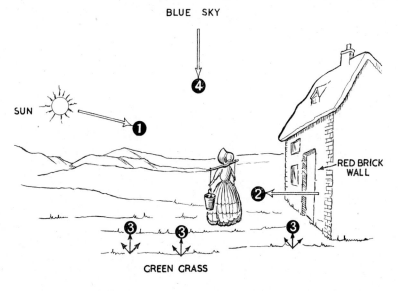

1 **PALE GOLD LIGHT (DIRECT)**   3 **GREENISH LIGHT (REFLECTED)**

2 **REDDISH LIGHT (REFLECTED)**   4 **BLUISH LIGHT (DIRECT)**

FIG. 68. LIGHT FROM FOUR DIRECTIONS IN VARYING COLOURS
The Woman in this picture would be directly lighted by (1) the Sun and (4) the Sky; and also by reflected light from (2) Red Brick Wall, (3) Grass. She would thus be lighted from four different directions in light of varying colours.

degree of saturation in colours of any one group. Thus, Straw No. 3 is a very de-saturated colour, while Amber No. 4 is fully and Orange No. 5 partly more saturated. This means that when Straw No. 3 and Amber No. 4 filters are used on opposite sides of a person, the result is not very pleasing, whereas if both colours had the same degree of saturation, a fairly harmonious effect would be achieved. Amber No. 4, for example, can be matched by a mixture of red and green light, whereas Straw No. 3 can be matched by equal quantities of red, green, and white light. Since saturation concerns the amount of white light present in a colour mixture, it will be seen

147

that the tone level of these two colours is very different; for a balanced composition, they are not suitable as a pair of harmonized colours.

Colour hues obtained from mixtures of white, red, green, and blue circuits in four-colour equipment possess a great advantage over those obtained from single lighting units with gelatine filters of a desired hue, because the former can be adjusted not only in colour hue but in degree of saturation. Thus, yellow and orange light can be projected on opposite sides of a person and the colours adjusted both in hue and to the required degree of saturation. As explained in Chapter 1, red, green, and blue light of the correct hue will act as primary colours and when combined in different proportions will enable almost any known colour hue to be provided. If, in addition, a full circuit of white light is available, any saturated colour hue obtained from the primary colours can be de-saturated to the required degree by the introduction of a certain amount of white light. When white or near-white light is required the fourth circuit of white can be used, either alone or in conjunction with one or more of the primary colours, thus providing the required intensity of illumination for straight stage lighting.

The Delicolor Control System described on page 87 provides an alternative to the routine of using gelatine filters of the required colour, because in conjunction with suitable four-colour equipment, colour mixtures corresponding to the entire gelatine range can be provided with ease. Furthermore, the degree of saturation can be adjusted, whereas with gelatine filters they are fixed and unchangeable.

The light from gelatine filters can be made less saturated by the use of two or three thicknesses at the same time; with many colours, however, there is also a change in hue when two or three thicknesses are utilized, and this is not always desired.

LIGHTING OF THE SETTING

When realism is required, there is little excuse for the use of coloured light through door openings, windows, etc., unless the colour of the light can be justified by reflection either from a coloured surface or directly from light that logically might exist. Thus, pale pink light would hardly be obtained from a yellow light source or from reflections off a green surface. However, there is artistic justification for exaggeration of the intensity and colour of the light, providing that both colour and direction are justified to some extent by the lay-out of the setting.

In musical comedy, pantomimes, etc., both indoor and outdoor settings are frequently lighted from wings and overhead by richly coloured light that, by no possible stretch of imagination, could ever happen in nature or fact. A woodland scene lighted with yellow wing floods on either side of the stage, with mauve and peacock-blue lights from overhead, presents an impossible combination as far as realism is concerned. This sort of thing, however, may be quite permissible in musical comedy and revue, when realism is not required, but even then the scenery is often constructed and painted to look real, and the extravagant use of coloured light without any basis on fact will sometimes tend to present a vulgar rather than a pleasing effect. Fantasy can be achieved even with a realistic setting, by keeping to certain fundamentals as, for example, the fact that the sun does not shine from two opposite directions at the same time.

Beautiful and imaginative lighting can be achieved on realistic settings by keeping to some semblance of nature's fundamentals but exaggerating them. If the Dominant Lighting bears some relation to fact, it is usually permissible to build up really vivid colour compositions, providing the relationship of the other colours to the Dominant Light is based on sound artistic principles. Thus, if there is an open air scene at night-time, the Dominant Light can be very pale blue-green from overhead, and other colours related to this dominant colour can be introduced from other directions, providing the fundamentals of colour harmony are maintained and the Dominant Lighting is not swamped.

A mistake sometimes made is to pour sunbeams through windows on opposite sides of a room. This is, of course, impossible in nature: if sunbeams come from one side, the light seen from the opposite window must be reflected light. This reflected light might come from the sky, or a wall, field, flower-beds, and so on, and the presence of any of these can be suggested by the tint of the light selected. If the light is assumed to come from the sky, it should have a bluish tinge, but if from trees or bushes outside the window, then a greenish tinge may be introduced. If the lighting is planned on these lines, it is, of course, permissible to project two or three different coloured lights through the one window.

When there is a powerful Dominant Colour-tinted Light from a side direction, there will be a tendency for any low intensity white lighting from the opposite side to take on a complementary colour tint; this is due to the factor of simultaneous contrast. With artistic licence, this tendency can be exaggerated and a touch of complementary coloured light added, even in scenes where realism is required. Thus, in an interior setting with pale or neutral coloured walls, it will be quite permissible to balance powerful overhead lighting with lighting from the footlights that has in it a tinge of colour complementary to the overhead lighting.

Of course, in a stage production, it is not possible to keep strictly to realism but only to a convention of realism, otherwise, spotlights in the auditorium, for example, would be out of the question. It is wise, however, not to let the lighting stray too far from the bounds of reality, and if delightful and delicate lighting effects are found that are not quite justified by the setting, then it may be possible to introduce new features into the scene to adjust the matter. The general requirements for the lighting should be considered, of course, before a final decision is made concerning the design and construction of the setting.

Emphasis can be given to a person or object by lighting of higher intensity than elsewhere. For this reason, among others, it is usual to illuminate the most important parts of the acting area to a higher intensity than the remainder of the stage. Areas of varying lighting intensity should be arranged with the same sense of balance and value as would be applied to the general décor. The various areas of lighting should be merged into one lighting composition based on sound æsthetic principles. Spotlights should not be used at random or left to be an afterthought when the décor is completed, but lighting should be considered as part of the general arrangement.

The balance of many scenes is upset by too high an intensity of light on flats behind door openings, etc., caused through the proximity of powerful floodlights that illuminate these areas to a higher intensity than the main part of the scene. Generally speaking, these areas are not really important and there is little justification for lighting them in a manner that suggests that they have strong dramatic value. Again, passageways and rooms beyond are not usually lighted in strongly coloured light; but if coloured light must be used, then let it fit in with the general colour composition of the whole setting and not act as a discordant note.

It is well known that painted scenery looks much better when viewed under stage lighting, but the extent to which lighting can improve the appearance is not always realized. The use of slightly colour-tinted light will cause certain colours in the painting to stand out more vividly, and by the choice of a suitable tint the three-dimensional aspect of the painting may be enhanced. Painters of stage scenery frequently provide coloured shadows to create a three-dimensional appearance. If the lighting is slightly tinted in a hue corresponding to the colour of the shadows, they will appear more real and thus promote the semblance of actual three-dimensional objects.

When light is colour-tinted, it means that there is a predominance of a certain primary colour or colours in its composition, and all elements of the same colour or colours in pigments or dyes illuminated by this light will be brighter in appearance. Thus, light with a bluish tinge will cause the blue element in pigments, etc., to be emphasized, while light with a yellowish tinge will enhance the elements of red, green, and yellow in a painting. It is very interesting to watch a painted scene while different hues of lighting are being tried out, and to observe the variations in appearance.

Colour-tinted light harmonizes the different colours in a painting or setting and tends to bring together colours that are quite different from each other. Thus, scenes can be painted in strong separated colours which afterwards can be unified on the stage by the use of colour-tinted light. A landscape scene showing objects of widely different colours, as, for example, red wall, green bush, yellow thatched roof, mauve flowers, and blue sky, can be harmonized by being flooded with slightly colour-tinted light.

Painters often employ bright or coloured outlines in their compositions, and these can be enhanced by the use of light with a corresponding colour-tint. Dullish colours can be given more lift, and various colours that are separated from each other by coloured outlines can be unified or more distinctly contrasted, according to the colour of the illumination. Coloured outlines may be made to glow at the same time as changes are effected in the appearance of the colour of the enclosed areas.

Colours can be presented under stage lighting in a manner quite impossible to the ordinary artist, who, for the luminosity of his colours, has to rely upon the percentage they reflect of the incident light. It is impossible for a fully saturated blue in a painting to have a greater luminosity than yellow when the design is seen under ordinary lighting; but with stage lighting, the blue areas can be made to exceed the luminosity of the yellow areas by the suitable use of colour-tinted light. Thus, by the use of coloured light in place of white light, an entirely new factor is introduced into the art of colour.

NEW ART OF LUMINOUS COLOUR

Designs in luminous colour can be created by projecting light of different colours from various angles on to three-dimensional white or lightly coloured objects. The most beautiful colour compositions can be created in this manner and the colours can have a luminosity that it is impossible to achieve by any other means. The luminosity of any colour can be increased or reduced at will, so that a rich blue, for example, can be made to appear brighter than a yellow. Furthermore, the colour of the lighting can be changed so that one colour arrangement can be dissolved into another. A new art of animated colour is now unfolding, and it is difficult to foresee the final effect it is likely to have on stage décor and presentation.

Changeable colour lighting can be made to impart varying interests and meanings to basic design and form, and can cause appearances to change in harmony with different dramatic values. Delicate or startling changes can be effected because colours can be made to succeed each other in any desired order, whereas with painted scenes the amount of change is limited.

Coloured light has a beautiful, luminous quality difficult, if not impossible, to achieve by dyes and pigments. When white or neutral-coloured surfaces are coloured by means of light, it is useful to designate the resultant hue as luminous colour. The creation of colour compositions in luminous colour implies a new approach to the subject of colour, because there is a very marked difference between coloured design presented by pigments and revealed by light, and colour compositions created by light itself.

Luminous colour can be utilized to impart beauty rather than to reveal beauty and can continually unfold new aspects. Form and outline can be accentuated and appearances correctly allied to dramatic values.

So far, scenic settings have been mainly constructed of painted canvas pieces or of draperies, and little use has yet been made of three-dimensional white set pieces illuminated from various angles in luminous colour. While painted scenes will continue to be employed for realistic settings, there is a large field for the employment of white set pieces with luminous colour for spectacular production scenes. One or two white columns, in conjunction with some three-dimensional set pieces or simple geometric shapes, can be transformed by luminous colour into a spectacle of very great beauty. The colours can merge into other colours so that a sequence of unfolding colour harmonies is provided. Settings of this nature are best seen against a white or cyclorama background suitably flooded in coloured light.

This new art reveals and constitutes form largely by its own qualities, and cannot be restricted to the narrower limits of static colour schemes. As a succession of harmonies can be presented on a surface, the latter is not an end in itself, but a means to an end.

With luminous colour, a succession of beautiful appearances can be presented, but since each differs from all the others, they cannot all be exact representations of the actual area so treated. An artist normally creates by colour design a surface that is intended to be viewed as actually treated, whereas with luminous colour the surface is intended only as a medium for the reflection of light.

Further information concerning opportunities for the application of luminous colour to production technique will be found in Chapter 13.

THE CHOICE AND EFFECT OF COLOURED LIGHT ON COLOURED COSTUMES AND SETTINGS

STARTLING changes can often be produced by throwing monochromatic or richly coloured light upon objects of a different hue. Subtle changes also take place in the appearance of colours when they are viewed under slightly colour-tinted light. Colour-tinted light is used to a far greater extent on the stage than white light and the effect of coloured light on coloured objects must be taken into account.

APPEARANCE OF COLOURS

In Chapter 1 the factors of colour vision and the colour composition of light for different colours are discussed, and it is shown that an object appears to be coloured because it reflects light rays corresponding to that colour into the eye of the beholder. Thus, a yellow costume appears to be yellow under normal lighting because it selectively reflects the wave-lengths of light corresponding to red, yellow, and green, and absorbs the remaining rays. Under a deep blue light, the costume would no longer appear yellow but almost black, as the incident light would not contain the light rays necessary to build up a sensation of yellow and, as already shown, the garment absorbs any other wave-lengths of light, so that the incident blue light would be almost totally absorbed.

It is not difficult to foresee the effect that colour-tinted light will have on coloured objects of a different hue, if the colour composition of the light and the pigments is understood. The three-colour theory of colour vision is quite adequate for this purpose, and it is only necessary to comprehend the approximate proportions of red, green, and blue light in the illuminant, and the reflective qualities corresponding to these colours in the object that is illuminated. Thus, a yellow material will imply that red and green light will be reflected and blue light absorbed, and this means that red and green must be present in the illuminant if the material is to be seen as yellow.

One normally speaks of colour as it would be viewed in daylight, and if the hue is to appear the same under artificial light it is necessary for the reflected light rays to be present to the same degree in the illuminant as in daylight. When thinking in terms of three primary colours of light, it is usual to assume that normal white light corresponds to equal intensities of the three primary colours, red, green, and blue, and this usually means a greater lamp load in the case of blue.

The composition of the main colour hues of light is shown on pages 3 to 8. It will quickly be seen that some introduction of the primary colour or colours not used in a mixture will have the effect of de-saturating the colour, since when all three primary colours are present to any degree the colour mixture begins to approach white.

In daylight an orange-coloured object reflects all the red incident rays, but only partly reflects the green rays of light. If an artificial illuminant possesses the same proportion of red and green light as in daylight, the colour of the orange object will be unchanged. But if, for example, there is a greater preponderance of red in the illuminant, then the colour of the object will be changed, because the proportion of red light reflected will be greater than normal, causing the colour hue to change from orange nearer to red in appearance. On the other hand, if green light exceeds red light in the illuminant, the resultant reflection of light rays will produce an appearance much nearer yellow than orange in hue. If the illuminant emits only green and blue light, however, the appearance of this object will change from orange to green, because the absence of red light means that no red rays can be reflected, and of green and blue light the object will reflect only the green rays, because, as already shown, it normally absorbs blue light. (See Plate III.)

CHOICE OF FABRICS

The appearance of costumes and dresses is governed not only by their colour but also by the materials of which they are composed. Thus shiny material gives specular surface reflections of the incident light as well as normal diffuse reflections where selective colour absorption may have taken place. A mat fabric, however, will give little or no such surface reflection of light but will reflect only light corresponding in colour to its own make-up.

Briefly, materials can be divided into three classes: (a) mat, (b) shiny, and (c) transparent or semi-transparent. When light falls upon shiny materials, a certain amount of specular reflection takes place in addition to spread and diffuse reflection. Mat materials give only diffuse reflection; while transparent or semi-transparent materials transmit a certain amount of the incident light. The diffuse reflection from shiny materials gives the normal colour appearance of the fabric; but in addition, the glossy surface, at certain angles, will reflect incident light rays direct into the eye of the beholder without any colour absorption taking place, and at these positions the fabric gleams and takes on the colour of the incident light. Thus, black satin, at certain angles, will reflect light of any colour quite well, whereas black serge would hardly reflect any light.

Dresses made of satin or other glossy materials must therefore be lighted with great care if they are to maintain an appearance corresponding to the normal colour of the material. A pale blue satin lighted by white lights wrongly placed may give so many bright surface reflections of incident light as to make perception of the pale colour-tint rather difficult. On the other hand, the appearance may be enhanced if the incident light is coloured to correspond with the colour of the fabric, so that the high-lights give the right impression of colour. It is important, of course, that the material is not generally lighted with colour-tinted light of a different hue, or not only will the pale blue shade of the material change in appearance but it will be somewhat submerged by the presence of coloured high-lights of a different hue.

Coloured high-lights of a hue different from that of the material, however, can be made to enhance the latter if the fabric is first flooded in light tinted to the correct colour and is then made to gleam by reflection of light of a near-colour, the relationship of these two coloured lights being based, say, on Rood's Law (see page 136). Thus, a pale blue dress would be first flooded in pale blue light, and the high-lights added in pale green or pale green-blue, the latter two being even more pale in hue than the blue. If the right balance is struck, the appearance of the dress will be enhanced without departing from its natural main colour.

Costumes and dresses made of shiny materials can often be lighted without consideration for their normal colour, providing a pleasant effect is obtained. In these cases, all the factors of colour contrast, harmony, and discord can be utilized and colour compositions built up to provide every kind of effect. Very vivid effects will always be caused by lighting from different directions in contrasting colours, the maximum of contrast being obtained when the lights are complementary to each other in hue.

Mat materials provide little in the way of surface reflection, although some fabrics do have a certain amount of gloss. The appearance will depend upon the colour of the light reflected from the material and, if the normal colour appearance is to be retained, it is important that the illuminant should possess the required proportions of the essential primary colours. Colour-tinted light means that there is a predominance of one or two of the primary colours, and this is bound to effect a change in the appearance of most coloured fabrics. Mat materials tend to change in colour under stage lighting rather more than shiny materials, so when startling changes in the colour materials are required for stage effect, mat materials are usually the most impressive.

When a dress made of a mat material has plenty of folds, emphasis can be given to the normal colour by lighting the dress mainly in white or in a colour-tinted light corresponding to the normal hue of the dress, with, in addition, a little light of a near colour playing on to the folds, which tends to build up the colour appearance of the remainder of the dress. The near colour should be chosen in much the same way as that discussed above for the satin dress.

Sometimes the appearance of a dress is enhanced by the use of light of a colour different from that of the dress, because, although a change takes place, the colour value of the material may be sharpened and appear more pleasing than the original colour. This is particularly the case when a dress is viewed against a colourful setting, because the various colours on the stage can be unified and brought together by the judicious use of colour-tinted light. Even colours that would normally jar when seen together can be harmonized to some extent in this way.

When a number of dresses differing in design and colour are seen on the stage at the same time, they can be blended into one colour composition by lighting of the correct colour. Sharp contrasts of colour can be either accentuated or diminished, and elements of colour common to many dresses can be enhanced, according to the ideas of the producer. Furthermore, the different colours can be more easily blended together for a single dramatic effect, should this be necessary. In musical comedy and revue there are also great possibilities of producing a series of different effects by various changes in the colour and arrangement of the lighting.

STUNT AND COLOUR CHANGING EFFECTS ON COSTUMES AND DESIGNS

Since Samoiloff introduced his colour change effects at the London Hippodrome over twenty years ago, there has been a continuing interest in the possibilities of using light for striking changes in the appearance of persons and scenery. By means of light, girls in bathing costumes can be changed into nudes, white men into negroes, dresses can be made to disappear, designs can be varied, and scenery changed in appearance. Usually there is one fundamental principle behind these changes, i.e. the use of coloured light on carefully chosen colours.

If a monochromatic red light is thrown on to a monochromatic blue dress, the latter appears to be dead black; but if lighted in blue light or in any light containing the element of blue, it will, of course, resume its normal appearance. If the blue dress has a black design upon it, this will be invisible under the red light because the whole dress appears black, but under other lighting a black design will be visible against the blue ground. Thus, a change from red to blue light will cause a seemingly black dress to change in appearance to a blue dress with a design on it.

Now if the object is mainly black in itself but has blue areas with a red design upon them (both blue and red colours being monochromatic), the apparent shape of the coloured areas will change when the lights are switched from red to blue. Under monochromatic red light the blue portion of the coloured areas will therefore appear black and merge with the normal black portions of the object, while the red design will stand out strongly against a black ground, because it is lighted in red light. The object will, therefore, appear black with a pattern corresponding to the red portion only of the actual design. Under monochromatic blue light, the red portion of the design will appear black, while the blue areas will stand out vividly in blue. Thus, both the apparent shape and colour of the coloured areas will be changed.

If the colours employed in the design are secondary colours such as yellow or mauve, they will turn black under monochromatic light only if the pigments are quite void of any element of colour corresponding to the light. Thus, a rich mauve or cerise will turn black under a monochromatic green light, but if the mauve is more of a pink, i.e. tends to become a pastel colour, then definitely it will not appear black under any monochromatic lighting

Secondary and pastel colours will generally yield intriguing changes in hue when seen under light of many different colours. Thus, yellow and mauve in a design both appear as different shades of red under monochromatic red light, and as shades of green and blue under peacock blue light. Excellent results are nearly always obtained if a brightly coloured design in secondary colours is superimposed on a bright peacock blue material with a mat surface.

CHANGING THE APPEARANCE OF COLOURS

The change in appearance of some of the main saturated colours, when viewed under lighting of many different colours (also saturated), is shown on the next page.

It will be appreciated that the appearance of the colours will not be as shown if the object has a shiny surface, because specular reflections of light will take place, and, if these directly enter the eye of the beholder, the object at these points will appear to take on the colour of the lighting.

ACTUAL COLOUR OF OBJECT	APPEARANCE UNDER RED LIGHT	APPEARANCE UNDER YELLOW LIGHT	APPEARANCE UNDER GREEN LIGHT	APPEARANCE UNDER PEACOCK BLUE LIGHT	APPEARANCE UNDER BLUE LIGHT	APPEARANCE UNDER CERISE LIGHT
Red	Red	Red	Dark Brown	Black	Purple-Black	Red
Orange	Red	Yellow	Dark Green	Dark Green	Black	Red
Yellow	Red	Yellow	Green	Green	Black	Red
Yellow-Green	Grey	Yellow-Green	Green	Green	Purple-Black	Dull Red
Green	Black	Green	Green	Green	Near-Black	Dark Purple
Peacock-Blue	Black	Green	Green	Peacock-Blue	Blue	Blue
Blue	Black	Black	Greenish-Black	Blue	Blue	Blue
Violet	Dark Red	Dull Red	Black	Blue	Blue	Violet
Magenta	Red	Red	Black	Blue	Blue	Cerise

BATHING BELLE TO NUDE EFFECT

A girl in a bathing costume can be made to appear almost a nude under pleasing lighting, provided that (a) the costume is tightly fitting everywhere, and (b) the colour of the costume is a fairly pastel colour, preferably pink or rose or some other tint deeper than but near to flesh colour. When the model is lighted in a tint complementary to the colour of the costume, the latter will be seen in a marked degree and will be clearly distinguishable from the body. When light of a colour corresponding to the costume is flooded on to the model, both limbs and costume will take on the same colour hue, and it will then be difficult to distinguish the actual costume. The colour change effect is fairly easy to obtain, and the most difficult part of this effect is to get a bathing costume to fit without wrinkling; under the " nude " lighting, the wrinkles rather spoil the effect and suggest the presence of a costume.

THE WHITE MAN TO NEGRO EFFECT

A white man can appear to change into a negro, or vice versa, by means of monochromatic red and green light and his own make-up. If the face, hands, etc., are covered in vermilion, when viewed under a monochromatic red light the appearance will be that of a normal person seen under red light, because there is nothing to suggest the presence of the vermilion make-up. When the light is changed to a monochromatic green hue, the vermilion make-up takes on the appearance of a deep brown and, if the make-up has been properly applied, a very good illusion of a negro is created.

To achieve this result, the gelatine filters used from the range shown on page 35 should be Red No. 6 and Green No. 39.

The appearance of the clothing can be made to change at the same time as the person's face if the colours are properly worked out. Thus, if the white man is supposed to be in evening dress, the presence of vermilion stripes on the shirt front will not be seen under the red light; but when the lighting is changed to green, they will appear vividly in dark brown. Similarly, the white tie can be given spots, and various other changes can be devised to appear in the clothing.

Some years ago, the writer produced a scene in which a number of Arabs on the stage in white robes, etc., were changed in appearance, by means of lighting only, to officers of the French Foreign Legion. The scenery was changed at the same time from a view of the desert to the interior of a fort. The lighting filters used on this occasion were Blue No. 19 gelatine for the Arab scene, and Red No. 6 gelatine for the interior of the fort. Vermilion make-up was used on the faces, and although the blue light turned this almost black (instead of the brown appearance obtained under green light) the blue light was necessary because the Arab scene was taking place at night.

CHANGES IN THE APPEARANCE OF SCENERY

Scenery can be designed to give very marked changes in appearance when illuminated in light of different colours, and the pigments and materials usually employed by scenic artists give very good results indeed for this purpose. The principles already outlined for the treatment of dresses and make-up apply also to scenic designs. It is not very difficult to work out a combination of colours that will enable one scenic design to appear as two distinctly different scenes when viewed under suitable lighting.

A canvas cloth, for example, can be painted so as to represent the Taj Mahal when seen under blue lighting, and an English landscape under red lighting. This is achieved by first of all painting the Taj Mahal scene in monochromatic red paint on a white ground, and then, when the paint is dry, superimposing a design of an English countryside, carried out in a monochromatic blue paint, on the first design. It is a good idea for the artist, while carrying out the painting, to view the canvas from time to time through pieces of red and blue gelatine. Then he can be sure that

(a) Normal appearance (seen under red light).

(b) Negro appearance (seen under green light).

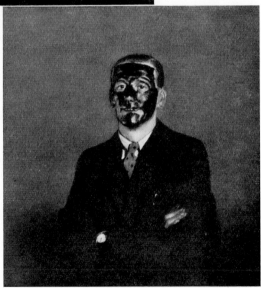

FIG. 69. WHITE MAN TO NEGRO EFFECT

This man's face is partly covered with a pure red make-up and under red light it is impossible to distinguish the areas in question. Under green light, however, the make-up takes on a dark brown appearance and can be easily distinguished from the parts of the face that have not been treated.

161

he is using the right density of colour for it to disappear against the white ground when seen under a light produced by the appropriate colour filter (see Fig. 70).

When the canvas is illuminated with red light, those parts of the design carried out in red against the white background disappear from view, and only the design carried out in blue pigment is seen,

FIG. 70. TWO VIEWS OF THE SAME SCENE AS REVEALED UNDER
TWO DIFFERENT LIGHTING ARRANGEMENTS
A Scene can be instantly changed in appearance by means of lighting.

the red light showing this up as a dark area. Where the blue pigment has been superimposed on part of the red design, a grey appearance is produced, and this will appear to fit exactly into the remainder of the design. When the lighting is changed to blue, those parts of the design in blue pigment against the white canvas disappear from view, and only the design carried out in red pigment is seen, the blue light turning this almost black in appearance. Where the blue design has been superimposed on the red pigment, the dark grey is lost in the general monochromatic appearance of the design.

PART IV. PRACTICAL LIGHTING FOR STAGE PRODUCTIONS

■

CHAPTER 12

SUGGESTIONS FOR LIGHTING A PLAY

THE action of most plays takes place in an interior setting, and outdoor scenes are less often used. Consequently, lighting arrangements for many plays are governed by the fact that overhead lighting equipment can be used only to a limited extent (except near the front of the stage), owing to the presence of a scenic ceiling. Footlights play an important part because, in the absence of several overhead battens, they have to provide much of the general illumination, especially of the walls and ceiling of an interior. Spot batten equipment is almost essential.

When vertical proscenium battens are available, they are often employed in addition to the footlights, when the setting lends itself to their use. Circle spotlights also are very useful, for providing additional front illumination. Perch spotlights and various portable spotlights and floodlights are utilized for local effects. Sometimes a sky-cloth or backcloth is visible, and is illuminated by overhead and/or portable equipment. Spot booms are sometimes used.

Generally, the spot batten equipment and footlights are most important, the remaining equipment being used to augment their illumination and to provide various local effects. Front-of-house arc spotlights are not usually employed for " pin spotting " certain artists, since the stage itself is lighted with the correct dramatic balance and the producer arranges matters so that artists are placed to get the desired illumination at appropriate points in the play.

ARRANGING THE SPOT BATTEN

When the lighting of an interior scene is being planned, it is well to start by considering the setting of the spotlights on the spot batten equipment, and the spotlights available for the scene should first be correctly angled. Certain spotlights may have to be tilted to direct light on to some portion of the setting or acting area to provide a specific effect, but spotlights available for the general illumination are usually angled towards the main part of the acting area. This arrangement prevents or restricts the spotlights from lighting up adjacent scenery, and builds up the intensity of illumination towards the centre of the stage. Of course, the action of the play may require variation of intensity on different parts of the acting

163

area, and the spotlights are then arranged to provide this. Apart from local effects, however, it is usual to light the scenery to a lower intensity than the acting area.

When prismatic lensplate spotlights are comprised in the spot batten the beams of light are soft-edged; but sometimes the spotlights are of the type that give a clear-cut circle of light, and frosted filters can then be employed to soften the light and smooth out the clear-cut edge. Soft-edged beams are particularly desirable when light from a spotlight impinges on part of the scenery.

COLOUR FILTERS FOR BATTEN SPOTLIGHTS

White light is seldom used alone, because the effect is somewhat harsh, and it is usual to fit some or all of the spotlights with colour filters. Even when the effect of white light is desired, it is generally better to achieve this by a mixture of light from spotlights giving slightly different colours. For example, spotlights alternately fitted with Pale Gold No. 52 and Pale Rose No. 54 filters will give a very pleasing effect. Alternatively, white light from a number of spotlights can be mingled with light from other spotlights fitted with colour filters, so that the white is just softened a little.

Spotlights used in this manner can be employed to build up a mosaic of slightly different colour-tinted lights, which give the effect of a broken white. The effect is most attractive and has been aptly called plastic lighting. Subtle variations in lighting intensity and colour are effected, and added interest is given to people moving about the stage.

Some three dozen colour filter tints are in frequent use and the possible arrangements of spotlights with different filters are legion. Stage lighting is as much a matter of individual taste and arrangement as is stage décor, and it is impossible to make dogmatic statements and fix hard and fast rules as to the arrangement of colours. The subject can be clarified, however, if it is remembered that a number of the standard gelatine tints are really not suitable for near-white lighting, and that, for this purpose, consideration need be given only to a smaller range of tints, numbering approximately fourteen colours.

The standard gelatine range of about thirty-six popular colours includes a number of saturated colours as well as very pale and semi-pastel tints. The deeper hues are seldom required for the straight lighting of a play, and generally the choice lies between the pastel colours and the very palest tints. The popular range of filters is not yet numbered in any scientific order, with saturated colours adjacent to other tints representing them in various stages of de-saturation. Therefore, it is difficult to list them in a manner that indicates the relationship between the various hues. However, the following arrangement gives some idea of the range of certain colours from deep hues to very pale tints. The remaining colours in the range are somewhat individual and cannot be correlated well in a table of this nature—

DEEP COLOURS	RICH COLOURS	PASTEL COLOURS	VERY PALE TINTS
Deep Blue No. 19	Medium Blue No. 32	Middle Blue No. 18	Steel Blue No. 17
Medium Amber No. 4	Amber No. 2	Straw No. 3	{ Yellow No. 50 { Gold No. 51 { Pale Gold No. 52
Orange No. 5	Deep Amber No. 33	——	——
Deep Rose No. 12	Deep Pink No. 11	Mid-Rose No. 10	Lavender No. 36
——	——	Light Rose No. 7	
Magenta No. 13	——	{ Salmon No. 8 { Middle Salmon No. 9	{ Pale Salmon No. 53 { Pale Rose No. 54
Green No. 39	Pea Green No. 21	——	

THREE-COLOUR BASIS FOR SPOTLIGHT FILTERS

It has been shown that the primary colours of light are red, green, and blue, and that the mingling of equal intensities of these three colours will produce white light. A row of spotlights, consecutively fitted with red, green, and blue colour filters produces white light where the colours are equally mixed, but broken effects on people and properties will be rather vivid, and perhaps too colourful for straight dramatic lighting. Consequently, pastel shades of these three colours would be more suitable. An ideal arrangement would be equal numbers of spotlights fitted in turn with pale red, pale green, and pale blue colour filters, but unfortunately these tints are not all available in the standard range of colour filters.

It will be seen from Plate I that the three secondary colours of light, i.e. magenta, yellow, and peacock blue, will also add up to white light, if equal proportions of these three colours are mingled. The resultant range of colour tints in the broken light is not so great as with red, green, and blue, but none the less, the results are very effective. Fortunately, the standard colour filter range does include pastel and some very pale tints of these three secondary colours, although in the case of peacock blue there is a quick jump from a rich green-blue to a pale steel blue. However, the missing colour can be replaced to some extent by using double thickness of the pale steel blue.

The following arrangement of standard colour filters indicates some of the available hues that approximate with various degrees of saturation to basic colours corresponding to the secondary colours of light, magenta, yellow, and peacock blue.

SECONDARY COLOURS (Slightly pastel)	PALER TONES	VERY PASTEL COLOURS	EXTREMELY PALE TINTS
Dark Pink No. 11	Mid-Rose No. 10	Lavender No. 36	Pale Rose No. 54
Medium Amber No. 4	{ Double Thickness of Pale Gold No. 52	Straw No. 3	{ Yellow No. 50, or Gold No. 51, or Pale Gold No. 52
Peacock Blue No. 15, or Moonlight Blue No. 16	————	{ Double Thickness of Steel Blue No. 17	Steel Blue No. 17

Spotlights on a batten, fitted in turn with colour filters from any one of these four groups, will give a final light that approximates to white, with delightful broken colour effects. The group selected depends upon the dramatic key of the lighting, and for straight plays the choice will usually be either the very pastel group or the fourth group. Thus, equal numbers of spotlights, fitted with filters Lavender No. 36, Straw No. 3, and double thickness Steel Blue No. 17, will give a slightly colourful effect, while equal numbers of spotlights fitted with Pale Rose No. 54, Pale Gold No. 52, and Steel Blue No. 17 will give a high intensity of broken white, with subtle variations only of tone on objects and people.

VARYING THE HUE OF SPOTLIGHTING

It will be appreciated that equal quantities of primary or secondary colours of light will tend finally to give a pure white light, whereas for dramatic purposes it is better to have the light slightly colour-tinted. In the examples just given, it may be necessary to reduce slightly the intensity of light from spotlights fitted with colour filters of one particular hue, in order to give the lighting the necessary off-white effect. Thus, in the case of Lavender No. 36, Straw No. 3, and double thickness Steel Blue No. 17, it will be necessary to reduce the intensity of the spotlights fitted with Steel Blue filters in order to give the light a warm tinge. Alternatively, the spotlights can be kept at full strength, but fewer of them can be fitted with the Steel Blue filters, so that there is a predominance of the other colours.

Usually, each spotlight on a spot batten is controlled by a separate dimmer, and then it is easy to vary the intensity from spotlights fitted with the same colour filters. An important advantage of using sets of three colour filters as just described is that, by variations in intensity of one or more of the three colours, the lighting can be given a pronounced tint towards blue, yellow, or pink. This is very useful not only for dramatic effects, but for providing lighting in keeping with the suggested time of day. If the setting is to be seen in night light, then pale blue lighting is available, while a predominance of the pink lighting is suitable for the set when artificial illumination is supposed to be in use. Predominance of the yellow lighting will give a bright sunlight effect.

It is not always convenient to employ several spotlights fitted with different colour filters, and sometimes single spotlights, or a number fitted with the same colour filter, have to give the desired effect. In these cases, the following suggestions for colour filters of spotlights lighting an *acting area* may be helpful—

Cold Light	Steel Blue No. 17.
Late Evening or even Night-time	Double thickness Steel Blue No. 17.
Night Lighting	Middle Blue No. 18.
Rich Sunlight	Straw No. 3.
Bright Sunlight	Pale Yellow No. 50.
Bright Interior Daylight . .	Gold No. 51, or Pale Gold No. 52.
Bright Interior Artificial Lighting .	Pale Salmon No. 53, or Pale Rose No. 54, or Lavender No. 36.
Rich Interior Artificial Lighting .	Light Rose No. 7, or Middle Salmon No. 9.

EFFECT OF LIGHT ON MAKE-UP

Consideration must be given to the effect of the colour of the lighting on make-up. It is generally found that, by themselves, Yellow No. 1, Amber No. 2, Straw No. 3, Medium Amber No. 4, Orange No. 5, and Amber No. 33, are rather hard on the ladies, although they are sometimes used with effect on male characters. The most effective standard colour filter for a feminine make-up is generally Lavender No. 36. Salmon No. 8, or Middle Salmon No. 9, can be effectively employed also, when it is convenient to use this type of hue.

Blue lighting or light with a pronounced bluish tinge usually has a very adverse effect on standard make-up and causes red and pinkish make-up colours to assume a dark, purple tinge. The effect is hardly noticeable under a Steel Blue No. 17 or even a Middle Blue No. 18, but with Dark Blue No. 19, Deep Blue No. 20, and Medium Blue No. 32, the change in the appearance of standard make-up is quite marked. Rich colours tend to flatten and take the colour detail out of make-up, and when the appearance of a person depends upon make-up care must be exercised on this point. It must be remembered, however, that modern lighting technique can replace make-up to a considerable extent, by the correct use of directional lighting, colour, and shadow. Lighting as a beauty aid can often be much more effective than stage make-up, and has the advantage of changeability, for lighting changes can be made in harmony with the dramatic values of a scene. Thus, a tragic appearance can be imparted to a character, and, if desired, this appearance can be intensified or lessened, according to the unfolding story.

VARIATIONS IN COLOURED LIGHT FROM STANDARD FILTERS

It is shown in Chapter 3 how the colour of light obtained from a colour filter varies with different light sources. There is quite a marked difference in the appearance of light obtained from most standard colour filters when used in spotlights, as opposed to magazine compartments in battens and footlights. A much higher intensity of light is projected through the colour filter on a spotlight at full strength, and furthermore, the spectrum of light from the filament of a 150-watt gas-filled lamp is not the same as the one belonging to, say, a 1000-watt gas-filled projector lamp.

Colour filters fitted in magazine compartment footlights and battens usually provide a duller colour than is provided by the same filters in spotlights. In order to get the same colour effect as provided by a spotlight, it may be necessary to fit the magazine compartments with filters of a deeper hue. Light passed through a pale colour filter appears to become more colourful as the lighting intensity is increased and, conversely, appears less colourful with a lower intensity.

The difference in the colour value of light obtained from a filter when used with lamps of various sizes must not be confused with the variations in intensity caused by dimming a lamp circuit. When a lamp is run at a reduced voltage, there is a change in the spectrum of emitted light: this produces a change in the colour of light received through a colour filter. Some colour filters are very sensitive to this factor: Lavender No. 36, for example, gives light of an appreciably different hue if the lamp behind the filter is dimmed. Careful thought must be given to this question or delicately balanced colour effects will be lost when the lighting is reduced in intensity.

FOOTLIGHTING FOR INTERIOR AND EXTERIOR SETTINGS

In an interior setting, only one or two overhead battens can usually be employed owing to the ceiling piece, and a good deal of the general illumination of the setting may have to be provided by the footlights. In the absence of many overhead battens, there is a tendency for the footlight to cast shadows of people and properties on to the setting. To overcome this tendency it is usual for frosted colour filters to be fitted in the magazine compartments of a footlight when an interior setting is to be illuminated. Generally, the colour filters chosen for the footlight are of a richer hue than are fitted in the overhead battens. Ordinary white light is seldom used alone as the effect is rather too harsh, and very pale colour filters, probably Gold No. 51 or Pale Gold No. 52, are often fitted instead of a circuit of white.

Magazine compartment footlights are generally wired on three- or four-colour circuits. It is usual to fit each circuit with a different set of filters, so that variations in the colour of the light are possible, and illumination amounting to near-white light can be obtained by using all the circuits together.

One footlight circuit is generally fitted with Gold No. 51 or Pale Gold No. 52 filters, in order to provide near-white light. Another circuit is usually fitted with pink filters, but, instead of the Lavender No. 36 or Pale Rose No. 54 filters favoured for spotlights, Light Rose No. 7 is more likely to be employed.

If any night effects are required, or perhaps even a cold light, the third circuit may be fitted with blue filters: these will be Steel Blue No. 17 for just a cold light or Middle Blue No. 18 for a pale blue light. If the equipment is arranged for four colours the remaining circuit may be a duplicate of one of the other three or it may be fitted with yellow filters, as, for example, Straw No. 3 for a pale yellow, or Medium Amber No. 4 for a richer hue.

The final selection of colour filters for a footlight, of course, will be based on the needs of the producer as regards the time of day, etc.; if there are no night scenes, for example, the blue filters may be omitted. Thus, for one recent production the footlights were provided with one circuit of Straw No. 3, one circuit of Light Rose No. 7, and two circuits of Gold No. 51.

When four-colour equipment employing white, red, green, and blue filters is available, the desired colour hues are obtained, of course, by mixture of the circuits.

OVERHEAD BATTENS FOR INTERIOR AND
EXTERIOR SETTINGS

It is probable that only one, or at the most two, overhead lighting battens can be used for the front lighting of an interior setting, as the remaining battens may be shut out by the ceiling piece. The main lighting for the acting area is then achieved by the overhead spot equipment, and the footlights provide much of the general illumination of the setting. In so far as the battens can be used, they add to the general illumination, and are usually fitted with colour filters similar to those provided in the footlights. It is probable, however, that paler colours may be used in certain cases, even, for example, Gold No. 51 or Lavender No. 36, compared with Medium Amber No. 4 or Light Rose No. 7 in the footlights.

Probably a backcloth or sky-cloth can be seen through windows or doors in the setting, and overhead battens can be used to illuminate this cloth. If a blue sky-cloth is employed and more than one time of day or night is to be represented, the batten illuminating it may be fitted entirely with blue colour filters, different circuits being fitted with, say, Steel Blue No. 17, Middle Blue No. 18, and Medium Blue No. 32, for mixture as desired. It is often found that excellent results are obtained on a blue sky-cloth as follows—

Day Effects	{Lavender No. 36. {Steel Blue No. 17.
Night Sky	Middle Blue No. 18.
Deep Night Sky	Medium Blue No. 32.

Sometimes a sky batten is fitted with two circuits of Middle Blue No. 18 and two circuits of Medium Blue No. 32: by combinations of these circuits different densities of blue light can be provided. The Carl Rosa Opera Company, for example, often use, in four-colour equipment, one circuit each of Middle Blue No. 18 and Dark Blue No. 19, and two circuits of Medium Blue No. 32.

The back-cloth may represent an exterior scene. If this is to be viewed in sunlight, a combination of circuits fitted with Dark Pink No. 11 and ordinary white light will generally give a very good effect. A combination of pink and white light gives a warmer effect than that of yellow and white light, which sometimes gives a slightly muddy effect.

AUXILIARY EQUIPMENT FOR A PLAY SETTING

Floodlights are often used to illuminate door backings etc., and are fitted with colour filters to avoid the harsh effect of white light. Straw No. 3 gives a good effect for sunlight and Steel Blue No. 17 for a cold evening light. Middle Blue No. 18 will give the effect of night light and Medium Blue No. 32 of deep night.

Portable spotlights are often used, either alone or in conjunction with floodlights, to project light through windows etc., and for a warm sunlight effect from a spotlight, Straw No. 3 is often utilized. Perch spotlights are frequently employed and are fitted with filters giving a near-white or pale colour-tinted light.

FLOODLIGHTS

The information given in this chapter concerning the effects obtained from colour filters used in conjunction with spotlights applies in most cases to filters used with individual floodlights, provided that lamps of 500 watts or more are used in the latter.

FIRE EFFECT

An interior setting often incorporates a fireplace. When the effect of firelight is desired, excellent results can be obtained from a spotlight mounted behind the opening, fitted with Dark Pink No. 11 filter with a centre hole cut away and filled with a piece of Orange No. 5.

CIRCLE AND BALCONY SPOTLIGHTS

The general illumination of an interior setting is often augmented by light from balcony or circle front spotlights. Generally these are fitted with colour filters of a pale tint: Straw No. 3, Lavender No. 36, and Pale Gold No. 52 are frequently employed.

REALISM OF LIGHTING

Some of the means to be used to achieve realism in lighting, and to avoid certain fundamental errors, have already been dealt with in Chapter 10, under the heading " Lighting of the Setting."

CHAPTER 13

SUGGESTIONS FOR LIGHTING OF OPERA, MUSICAL SHOWS, REVUE, AND BALLET

THE majority of plays are presented with interior settings, but musical shows are likely to include almost any type of stage scenery. Exterior settings are used to a considerable extent, while scenes of a novel and imaginative nature are frequently presented in revues. Even with straight settings, the general lighting is used to create effect rather than realism, although in the case of grand opera, it may be arranged on the same dramatic basis as a play.

Grand opera concerns drama that is mostly or wholly sung rather than spoken, but apart from this difference in expression it may be presented and lighted with the same realistic technique as in the spoken drama. Light opera, however, has intervals of spoken and often humorous dialogue between the musical numbers, and in these the lighting may be a little more fanciful. The light musical-dramatic nature and whimsical plot of some operettas call for imaginative treatment, and the lighting is often of the same type as is employed for the musical comedy or revue when lighting changes are used to create effect, without any regard to continuity of realism. Imaginative lighting based on sound artistic principles is usually employed for ballet.

LIGHTING OF GRAND OPERA

Since grand opera concerns drama with musical instead of spoken dialogue, it is usual to stage the production so that lighting and scenery maintain an appearance of realism. The production is generally more colourful than would be the case with a straight play, and the lighting therefore is richer and, while maintaining an effect of realism, rather more picturesque.

Usually there is more than one scene in the production; quite frequently interior and exterior settings occur in the same opera, so that the stage lighting equipment may be required to give several different types of effect.

The lighting is generally arranged on the same lines as for a straight play, utilizing one or more spot battens near the front of the stage in conjunction with footlights and overhead battens. Sometimes acting area floods are suspended between the battens. The fourth and fifth overhead battens are frequently fitted throughout with blue colour filters to give suitable lighting for a background sky-cloth, although sometimes a flood batten instead is used for this purpose. Auxiliary spotlights, floodlights, groundrows, etc., are used as the settings require, and spotlights on the perch platforms often play a useful part. Front-of-house arc spotlights are used to " pin-point " leading characters.

Covent Garden Opera House, London, is provided with a very elaborate lighting installation, and productions staged in this ·

FIG. 71. FRENCA BATTEN SPOTLIGHT
with Prismatic Lensplate, and fitted with magazine of four colour filter frames operated
by means of tracker wires from a control board in the Wings.

theatre have at their disposal a greater quantity of lighting equipment than is described above. Special features include a large curved cyclorama background, complete with multi-colour lighting and overhead lighting bridges, from which spotlights and special effects projectors can be manipulated. This installation is not indicative of the standard of stage lighting in other theatres in Great Britain, and it is not proposed to describe it in detail.

The Carl Rosa Opera Company utilizes a number of overhead batten spotlights at the front of the stage in conjunction with a number of perch and auxiliary spotlights. The first three overhead magazine compartment battens are usually fitted with colour filters suitable for the illumination of the acting area and scenery, while the back battens are fitted with a combination of blue filters for flooding a sky-cloth or backcloth. The colour filters are carefully chosen so that there is no need to change all the gelatine filters in the battens, footlights, etc., with each change of opera, and excellent lighting effects are skilfully obtained in each scene.

A useful combination of colours for the footlights and front stage battens, when four circuits are available, is as follows—

No. 1 Circuit . . White light.
No. 2 Circuit . . Light Rose No. 7 or Middle Salmon No. 9.
No. 3 Circuit . . Yellow No. 1, Amber No. 2, or Medium Amber No. 4.
No. 4 Circuit . . Medium Blue No. 32.

Battens used for sky-cloth lighting can be conveniently fitted with circuits Middle Blue No. 18, Dark Blue No. 19, and Medium Blue No. 32. Overhead batten spotlights employed for general illumination of the acting area can be fitted with an arrangement of colour filters on the basis suggested on pages 164 and 167.

COMIC AND LIGHT OPERA

The term comic opera at once suggests the Gilbert and Sullivan operas that are so popular everywhere. The professional presentation of these operas is in the hands of the D'Oyly Carte Opera Company, but amateur performances are given, by arrangement with the Company, by operatic societies in all parts of the country. There are, of course, many well-known comic and light operas by other composers.

The D'Oyly Carte Opera Company generally use lighting based on the combination of several very pale colours in the footlights and overhead battens, with the exception of the last batten, which is often fitted with pale blue filters throughout for the illumination of the backcloth. Overhead batten spotlights at the front of the stage also give a slightly colour-tinted light. The result is illumination of a relatively high intensity which can be varied easily in hue to suit the requirements of each scene.

Amateur performances of comic opera are sometimes presented on stages well provided with modern lighting equipment, but on other occasions the lighting facilities may be very simple.

If stage illumination depends almost entirely on footlights and battens, excellent results can be obtained by fitting the different circuits in each trough with pale yellow, pink, and pale blue colour filters.

Battens and footlights are usually wired on three or four circuits, and in the case of three circuit equipment, the following suggestions may be helpful as an alternative to the deeper colours suggested above for Grand Opera.

No. 1 Circuit	. .	Straw No. 3, Gold Tint No. 51, or Pale Gold No. 52.
No. 2 Circuit	. .	Steel Blue No. 17 or Middle Blue No. 18.
No. 3 Circuit	. .	Lavender No. 36.

When the apparatus is wired for four circuits, the equipment may be normally fitted with white, red, green, and blue colour filters, so that any desired colour hue can be obtained by blending these circuits in different proportions. In this case, excellent results can be obtained without changing the filters, as the lighting can be adjusted to the most appropriate tint by suitable mixture of the circuits. Otherwise, four circuits may be comprised of three circuits, as mentioned above, plus a fourth circuit of blue, the two blue circuits being arranged so that there is one of Steel Blue No. 17 and one of Middle Blue No. 18. When these circuits are all in use together, the resultant illumination will be almost white, but colour-tinted light can be quite easily obtained by partly or wholly taking out one or more of the circuits by means of switches or dimmers.

Sometimes the footlight and batten equipment may be wired on only one or two circuits. In the case of one circuit lighting, there is little that can be done except to provide white light or a mixture of light from, say, alternate lamps or compartments of different colours.

In the case of two circuits, one may conveniently be fitted with pale blue filters, and the other with alternate filters of pale pink and pale yellow. When both circuits are in use, white light is obtained, and by reduction of the strength of either circuit a useful range of tints can be procured. The effect can often be enhanced by arranging for the circuit with the yellow and pink filters to have, say, yellow or gold filters in the middle compartments, and pink filters in the units at each end of the footlight. The circuit with blue filters can also be arranged so that the last two or three compartments at each end are fitted with a deeper blue. When either or both of the circuits are in use, there will be a gradation of colour from the centre to the sides of the stage which, in conjunction with other stage lighting, adds interest and charm to the production.

Auditorium spotlights should be fitted with colour filters unless they play a relatively unimportant part in providing the required stage illumination. Since these spotlights are employed mainly for the illumination of characters, the filters should be of very pale colours, chosen perhaps from the following—

Straw No. 3.	Pale Salmon No. 53.
Gold Tint No. 51.	Pale Rose No. 54.
Pale Gold No. 52.	Steel Blue No. 17.
Lavender No. 36.	

Every effort should be made to provide a " modelling " effect on people on the stage, by mounting auditorium spotlights so that they illuminate the stage from different angles. Thus, a spotlight mounted at each side of the hall will provide better modelling than two spotlights mounted together in the centre. The modelling effect can be increased by the use of different colours from different directions, as, for example, pale gold from one side, and lavender from the other. When perch spotlights are available it is often possible to fit different colour filters at either side. Portable spotlights or floodlights, positioned in the stage wings, also can be arranged for colour contrast: they should be fitted with very pale filters when they play an important part in providing stage illumination, and deeper colour filters when they are only auxiliary to the main lighting.

When only two or three overhead battens are available, they are probably required for general illumination of the acting area; but when there is sufficient overhead equipment for one or two battens to be delegated to background lighting alone, it may be advisable to fit half, or even all, their circuits with blue filters. If circuits are fitted with Steel Blue No. 17, Middle Blue No. 18, and Medium Blue No. 32, a range of blue tints is available, and the batten can be used for day or night effects by variations in the strengths of the different circuits. Stages used for amateur performances, however, often rely upon single wing floodlights for the main illumination of the background and, in these cases, it will be necessary to change the filters for scenes indicating different times of the day or night.

When overhead batten spotlights are available, either as single units or in the form of a spot batten, they can be fitted with colour filters on the lines indicated on pages 164 to 167.

It is not always necessary to treat Gilbert and Sullivan productions on the basis of very light colours, and excellent results can sometimes be obtained by judicious use of richer colours. *The Mikado*, for instance, lends itself to very effective stage lighting and some of the musical numbers can be staged with dramatic colourful lighting. Right from the opening, when the curtain rises on the " Gentlemen of Japan," to the final curtain, there are numerous opportunities for staging individual numbers with romantic and effective lighting. The vivid costumes respond very effectively to changes in the colour of the illumination, and good use can be made of this factor in some of the chorus numbers.

While most of the lighting for Gilbert and Sullivan operas must be gay and bright, more colourful and dramatic lighting is suitable for other light operas. In some cases very similar lighting to that employed for grand opera can be utilized, providing that bright, gay lighting is available for certain scenes, and especially for humorous dialogue, etc.

Some light operas require the same kind of lighting as musical comedy, in fact it is a little difficult to draw a hard and fast line between the two. The type of lighting required is, of course, determined by the nature and treatment of the production.

MUSICAL COMEDY LIGHTING

Excellent opportunities for lighting effects are provided by most musical comedies. The story is always romantic and is presented in a picturesque manner. Lighting changes can be made without any regard to realism and, providing it is effective, almost any type of illumination may be employed.

The imaginative nature of the production is likely to require many very different arrangements of lighting. Humorous dialogue and comedy numbers will require white or near-white lighting; dance and chorus numbers require individual treatment; while romantic and other incidents necessitate suitable illumination. The lighting can be changed in colour and intensity at any time, without any basis of realism, provided it creates a suitable environment.

To provide the required colour changes in the general stage illumination, it is necessary for the footlights and battens to be provided with colour circuits that individually and collectively will give the desired range of effects.

Most productions require deep colours at some moments, and it is usual for the different circuits to be fitted with filters of fairly rich colour hue.

When the principle of three primary colours is understood, any desired colour hue can be obtained by fitting four-colour battens and footlights with circuits of white, Red No. 6, Blue No. 19, and Green No. 39 filters, and blending these in different proportions.

The presence of the white circuit enables pale and near-white colour hues to be obtained at high intensity, while suitable mixtures of the red, green, and blue circuits will provide the deeper colours. It is necessary for these four circuits to be controlled by separate dimmers so that these can be blended together in different proportions: in fact, special control equipment, as, for example, the Delicolor Controller (see Fig. 53), is recommended.

The primary colour system is not yet generally understood, and the usual practice is to fit the different circuits with colour filters according to individual choice. When four-colour battens and footlights are available, it is usual to arrange one circuit for white light (or near-white, e.g. Gold No. 51, Pale Gold No. 52), and then to fit the remaining circuits for amber, pink, and blue light. The colour filters chosen vary considerably and the footlights are often fitted with deeper colours than the overhead battens. Thus, Magenta No. 13 and Medium Blue No. 32 in the footlights may be accompanied by Dark Pink No. 11 and Middle Blue No. 18 in the battens. Sometimes the battens are fitted with different colours altogether to the footlights, but generally the first two or three overhead battens are fitted with similar colours to the footlights. The remaining battens are then arranged with suitable filters for background lighting.

The amber circuit is usually Medium Amber No. 4, but sometimes Amber No. 2 is employed. Two thicknesses of Pale Gold No. 52 give a very delightful effect which is often to be preferred to Straw No. 3 when a lighter colour is desired. When a circuit of white is also available, a deeper colour, as Orange No. 5 or Deep Amber No. 33, may be chosen, as the illumination can be lightened in hue by additional light from the white circuit.

The pink circuit is often either Light Rose No. 7, Middle Salmon No. 9, or Middle Rose No. 10, but with four-circuit equipment a deeper colour altogether is sometimes preferred, in which case Dark Pink No. 11, Deep Rose No. 12, or Magenta No. 13 may be used, as the white circuit can be used to lighten the hue when necessary. Red No. 6 is occasionally chosen as, by mixture with the blue circuit, a magenta can be obtained; but as red alone is seldom required, it is more usual to employ a pink or magenta circuit as just stated.

The blue circuit is usually fitted with Medium Blue No. 32 filters, although when only a blue-tinted light is required Middle Blue No. 18, which is a much paler colour, is employed. There are marked differences between the blue filters, which, in rising order of saturation are as follows—

Steel Blue No. 17.	Medium Blue No. 32.
Middle Blue No. 18.	Dark Blue No. 19.

Dark Blue No. 19 is the nearest to a pure blue and is the one most suitable for use as a primary colour. Deep Blue No. 20 is very

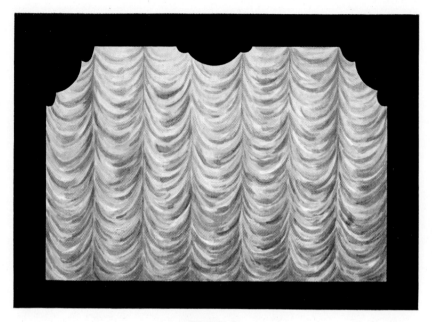

PLATE V

"The Tapestry of Dreams"

The Festoon Curtain with lighting in dynamic luminous colour was first used by the writer
under this title (see page 190).

similar, but often has a slight tinge of red in it. Steel Blue No. 17 is a very pale colour; two thicknesses make a useful intermediary colour between Steel Blue No. 17 and Middle Blue No. 18.

When battens and footlights are arranged for only three-colour circuits the white light is often omitted; instead, the yellow, pink, and blue circuits are of fairly medium hue so that there is no necessity to employ a circuit of white to de-saturate the colours. On other occasions the blue circuit, for example, may be omitted and the white retained, if there is no specific need for blue by itself in the production. Near-white light can be obtained by the use of yellow, pink, and blue light together, and the final hue can be decided by suitable adjustment in the intensity of one or more of these circuits. It is better for the filters to have approximately the same degree of saturation, and not to vary too much, or the near-white effect may be rather spoiled. The following suggestions may prove helpful—

Group 1: Pale Colours

One or two thicknesses of Straw No. 3 or Pale Gold No. 52.
Light Rose No. 7, Middle Salmon No. 9, or Middle Rose No. 10.
Middle Blue No. 18 or two thicknesses of Steel Blue No. 17.

Group 2: Medium Colours

Medium Amber No. 4.
Dark Pink No. 11.
Medium Blue No. 32.

Overhead battens for sky-cloth lighting are fitted with filters to suit the sky-cloth. Thus a blue sky-cloth may be lighted by one or more battens fitted throughout with Medium Blue No. 32 filters, or by various blue circuits including, say, Middle Blue No. 18, Medium Blue No. 32, and perhaps Dark Blue No. 19. Background cloths, however, may require light of other hues besides blue, and circuits of white and pink may be included. Thus the effect of sunrise on a foliage scene can be created by the joint use of white and Dark Pink No. 11 circuits.

It is usual to have one spot batten suspended near the front of the stage, and often there are additional spot or flood bars at positions further back-stage. The first spot batten is generally provided with spotlights that can be angled towards different parts of the acting area, but many of the lighting units on the additional spot battens are of a type that will throw the light more or less straight downwards. Sometimes there is a flood batten near the back of the set carrying a number of 500-watt or 1000-watt floodlights to provide high intensity of illumination of the backcloth.

The overhead front spotlights should be fitted with colour filters so that the majority of them are utilized on the three-colour basis described on page 165, and a final pale colour illumination is obtained where the beams overlap.

When the lighting is on a high key (i.e. is bright, fairly even, and delicately coloured) overlapping spotlights can be consecutively fitted with the following filters—

> Straw No. 3 or two thicknesses of Pale Gold No. 52.
> Lavender No. 36.
> Two thicknesses of Steel Blue No. 17 or Middle Blue No. 18.

When the lighting is on a lower key (i.e. is more dramatic and colourful with greater contrasts in intensity and colour) the following arrangement of filters may be useful—

> Amber No. 2 or Medium Amber No. 4.
> Light Rose No. 7 or Middle Rose No. 10 (alternatively Middle Salmon No. 9 or Salmon No. 8).
> Middle Blue No. 18.

It must be borne in mind that a light of a richer colour hue will be obtained from a filter used in a spotlight than from one in a magazine footlight or batten compartment. The deeper colours, such as Dark Pink No. 11, are therefore unsuitable for general illumination from spotlights, unless there is a definite reason for their use.

The light from spotlights using deep colour filters can, of course, be softened by further spotlights using paler colours; arrangements of this kind are sometimes favoured because, when skilfully employed, they increase the beauty of the broken colour effects. Thus, Medium Amber No. 4 can be used in conjunction with other spotlights fitted with, say, Gold No. 51. This method of lighting is generally based on harmonized colours rather than contrasting colours, and the broken colour effects are not so varied. A pale pink illumination can be achieved by a number of overlapping spotlights fitted with, say, Light Rose No. 7, Lavender No. 36, and Pale Rose No. 54 filters, giving broken colour effects of various shades of pink, or by spotlights fitted consecutively with Light Rose No. 7, Amber No. 2, and Middle Blue No. 18 filters, with the lighting intensity adjusted so that the predominate hue of the mixture is pale pink. Additional effect can be achieved by rounding off the illumination at each side of the stage with light of a different and deeper colour from each end of the spot batten. The pale pink illumination can, for example, merge into a deeper blue at each side, or even into a deeper pink, so that there is a shading off from the centre of the stage towards the wings.

Side lighting from the wings can play an important part in the lighting, and musical comedy scenery is generally constructed to allow wing lighting equipment to be employed. There is a tendency, however, to indulge in rather crude colour effects from wing spotlights and floodlights, and to depart from realism without any artistic compensation. While the general illumination from battens, footlights, and overhead spotlights is usually a pastel mixture, the wing lighting is often richly coloured and out of keeping with the general tone, and harsh colour contrasts are frequently to be seen.

Care should be taken to make the wing lighting fit in with the general colour composition, in both hue and tone, and contrasting colours should be chosen with due regard to the principles of pleasing contrasts (see page 137). The lighting of a realistic set should either be based fundamentally on realism, or be an imaginative creation based on sound artistic principles.

REVUE LIGHTING

An even greater variety of lighting effects is likely to be required in a modern revue, which, by its very nature, contains a number of items of a widely different type. Production sets of novel and imaginative design intermingle with straight numbers, while curtain settings and realistic scenery usually have a place in the sequence.

Almost every type of stage lighting finds a place in revue; the main difficulty is to obtain the many different effects from one arrangement of lighting equipment. While it is easy to obtain many different colour hues from footlights, overhead battens, and portable equipment, overhead spotlights and floodlights must be angled and fitted with filters to suit certain scenes and must so remain throughout the show.

Compositions of light and colour should be based on sound principles. If the fundamentals discussed in Chapter 10 are understood, it is not difficult to construct lighting arrangements that are pleasing, dramatically correct, and have æsthetic appeal. Stage lighting is an art, and the applications must always be completely individual.

There are unlimited arrangements of directional lighting and colour, and it is almost impossible to outline or classify the many different combinations. Some useful combinations of coloured light from battens and footlights which have occurred in the author's experience may, however, be interesting, and serve as a guide to other lighting arrangements.

Lighting equipment used in the following examples comprises footlights, two overhead lighting battens, and wing lighting from each side of the stage. A white, neutral, or very pale coloured setting is assumed and costumes, etc., also should be near-white or very slightly coloured.

Bluish Effect

Medium Blue No. 32 filters are fitted in all the equipment except the footlights, which are provided with Moonlight Blue No. 16 filters. The blue light from overhead and from both sides of the stage is contrasted by the greenish-blue light from the footlights. and a very delightful effect is obtained on the folds of draperies and costumes of a near-white colour.

A delightful alternative to this arrangement is to fit Medium Blue No. 32 filters throughout except in the footlights, which are provided with Moss Green No. 22 filters. There is a more marked contrast with this arrangement, which will be found most effective when a greenish-blue stage is required.

Another alternative is given below, when Lavender No. 36 can be effectively used as a contrast—

Footlights	.	.	.	.	.	Lavender No. 36.
No. 1 Batten		.	.	.	.	Medium Blue No. 32.
No. 2 Batten		.	.	.	.	Moonlight Blue No. 16.
P. Side Wings		.	.	.	.	Dark Blue No. 19.
O.P. Side Wings			.	.	.	Dark Blue No. 19.

Pinkish Effect

Dark Pink No. 11 filters are provided in the footlights and both overhead battens, and are contrasted by Moonlight Blue No. 16 from both sides of the stage. A soft romantic effect is obtained from this arrangement, with the contrasting colour coming from the sides.

An alternative to this arrangement, with the pink light coming from the sides, can be achieved as follows—

Footlights	.	.	.	.	Medium Blue No. 32.
No. 1 Batten		.	.	.	Light Green No. 23, with some white light added.
No. 2 Batten		.	.	.	Purple No. 25.
P. Side Wings		.	.	.	Middle Rose No. 10.
O.P. Side Wings			.	.	Middle Rose No. 10.

With this arrangement, the medium blue light from the footlights blends in quite closely with the rose and purple light, and the contrast is provided by the pale green light which comes from No. 1

overhead lighting batten. This arrangement is most impressive and looks very well on characters clad in satin or other shiny materials of a near-white colour.

The pink light itself can be used, just as a contrast, from both sides and from No. 2 lighting batten, provided that the main frontal illumination is by warm light from the footlights and No. 1 batten as follows—

Footlights	.	.	.	.	.	Pale Salmon No. 53.
No. 1 Batten	.	.	.	.	.	Orange No. 5.
No. 2 Batten	.	.	.	.	.	Dark Pink No. 11.
P. Side Wings	.	.	.	.	.	Mauve No. 26.
O.P. Side Wings	.	.	.	.	.	Mauve No. 26.

Yellow and Pink Effect

A very pleasing and somewhat unusual amber effect can be obtained by fitting all the equipment with Medium Amber No. 4 filters with the exception of No. 1 lighting batten, which is provided with Steel Blue No. 17 filters to give the necessary contrast.

A yellow and pale pink light can be blended with considerable effect by using Medium Amber No. 4 filters from both sides of the stage, and Lavender No. 36 filters in the footlights and in No. 1 batten. A touch of contrast is provided by the use of Medium Blue No. 32 filters in No. 2 lighting batten.

Amber can be used as a front contrast in a very pleasing arrangement, whereby Lavender No. 36 filters are used at each side of the stage with Steel Blue No. 17 filters in both lighting battens, and Deep Amber No. 33 filters in the footlights. The Steel Blue No. 17 and Lavender No. 36 colours blend into each other very nicely, leaving the contrast to be provided from the deep amber filters in the footlights.

A more complex arrangement, utilizing amber and pink light, is made up as follows—

Footlights	.	.	.	.	.	Salmon No. 8.
No. 1 Batten	.	.	.	.	.	Light Green No. 23.
No. 2 Batten	.	.	.	.	.	Dark Pink No. 11.
P. Side Wings	.	.	.	.	.	Medium Amber No. 4.
O.P. Side Wings	.	.	.	.	.	Medium Amber No. 4.

Planned Lighting

Revues lend themselves to elaborate and unusual lighting effects, because production numbers can be specially created for this purpose. Three-dimensional white scenery with rostrums and steps for the dancers can be made into a spectacle of unusual beauty by the use of directional lighting and contrasting colours. The effect can be greatly enhanced by showing the scenery against a cyclorama background flooded with coloured light. (See Plate IV.)

183

LIGHTING CUE SHEETS: "HERE COME THE BOYS"

ITEM..

F.O.H. O.P. Arc..
       P. Arc ....

CONTROLLED BY HOUSE SWITCHBOARD
   Floats ....
   Floats Frenca Spot O.P. ....
           Spot P. ....

CONTROLLED BY HOUSE SPOTBOARD
   F.O.H. Spots ....
   O.P. Tower (1) .... (2) ....
         (3) ....
   P. Tower (1) .... (2) ....
        (3) ....

CONTROLLED BY FURSE SPOTBOARD
     No. A Spot Bar   1 ....:................................
                   2 ....
                   3 ....
                   4 ....
                   5 ....
                   6 ....
                   7 ....
                   8 ....

     No. B Spot Bar   1 ....
                   2 ....
                   3 ....
                   4 ....
                   5 ....
                   6 ....
                   7 ....
                   8 ....

     No. C Spot Bar   1 ....
                   2 ....
                   3 ....
                   4 ....
                   5 ....
                   6 ....
                   7 ....
                   8 ....

CONTROLLED BY DELI BOARD A
   O.P. Pros. Lights ....
   O. Pros. Lights ....
   O.P. Cylo. No. 1 ....
   O.P. Cylo. No. 2 ....
   P. Cylo. No. 1 ....
   P. Cylo. No. 2 ....
   Troughs ....
           (Troughs cannot be used as well as Cylos.)

CONTROLLED BY DELI BOARD B
   O.P. Boomerang ....

CONTROLLED BY DELI BOARD C
   P. Boomerang ....

Cue One   " .... "

    House Switchboard ....
    House Spotboard
    Furse Spotboard
    Deli Board A
    Deli Board B
    Deli Board C

Cue Two   " .... "

    House Switchboard
    House Spotboard
    Furse Spotboard
    Deli Board A
    Deli Board B
    Deli Board C

Cue Three   " .... "

    House Switchboard
    House Spotboard
    Furse Spotboard
    Deli Board A
    Deli Board B
    Deli Board C

Cue Four   " .... "

    House Switchboard
    House Spotboard
    Furse Spotboard
    Deli Board A
    Deli Board B
    Deli Board C

Cue Five   " .... "

    House Switchboard
    House Spotboard
    Furse Spotboard
    Deli Board A
    Deli Board B
    Deli Board C

Cue Six   " .... "

    House Switchboard
    House Spotboard
    Furse Spotboard
    Deli Board A
    Deli Board B
    Deli Board C

Cue Seven   " .... "

    House Switchboard
    House Spotboard
    Furse Spotboard
    Deli Board A
    Deli Board B
    Deli Board C

(By Courtesy of J. Brandon-Thomas.)

Page 184 shows lighting as set for opening of item: a cue is given for each subsequent change of lighting required.

In one of Jack Hulbert's recent productions, including several production numbers based on this method, the beauty of the lighting effects fully justified the care spent on earlier planning. If it is desired to make a feature of the lighting, it is important that it should be considered from the beginning, and not at a later stage in the production, when the scenery, costumes, and décor have already been settled. Even the action must be taken into account, if the lighting is to play its proper part, and certainly no question of colour and material should be settled before the lighting has been considered. An expert on lighting should be present at all production conferences concerning these factors.

One of the main problems connected with elaborate lighting effects is the drawing up of adequate instructions to the switchboard operators and electricians so that the required effects can be obtained exactly as and when wanted, without undue difficulty. The lighting arrangements must be properly organized and the directions set down in a systematic and understandable manner, so that the stage director can get the required effects by giving a single cue. Considerable time and trouble can be saved by drawing up proper lighting cue sheets beforehand and having a supply of these available during rehearsals.

An excellent example is seen on pages 184 and 185 in the cue sheets drawn up by Mr. Jevan Brandon-Thomas in preparation for the Jack Hulbert production *Here Come the Boys*. The Stage Director keeps the master cue sheets and each individual operator has sheets with instructions filled in for those controls that are his responsibility. The instructions for each item or scene must start on a fresh sheet, and the sheets for each scene be clipped together.

BALLET

Ballet appeals especially to the eye, and by its very nature requires symbolic and artistic lighting. Form and movement are the essence of ballet, and, since lighting determines the final appearance of form, it is reasonable to assume that the lighting should be worked out with considerable care so that it plays an intelligent and deliberate part in the visual spectacle.

Classical ballet is frequently presented in blue-tinted light, as this creates an imaginative and ethereal environment. Blue-tinted light is particularly effective on white ballet dresses and is in keeping with much of the music employed.

Middle Blue No. 18 and Medium Blue No. 32 filters are frequently used for the general lighting, while Steel Blue No. 17 filters are used in front-of-house spotlights for " pin-pointing " different artists. Lavender No. 36 filters are very useful for providing a contrasting colour.

Battens and footlights can be conveniently fitted with circuits of Middle Blue No. 18, Medium Blue No. 32, and Lavender No. 36, although the Lavender can frequently be omitted from those battens that illuminate the backcloth, and instead another circuit of blue employed. If the difference between Steel Blue No. 17 and Middle Blue No. 18 for wing floods, etc., is too great, two thicknesses of Steel Blue No. 17 together may give the required results for certain tone contrasts.

Ballet is not confined to any one type of lighting. Indeed, it affords greater opportunites for individualism in lighting than do most forms of stage art. The lighting of ballet is a subject that can be discussed at considerable length, but for the purpose of this book it is sufficient to refer the reader to the principles already laid down in the five preceding chapters: these will facilitate the creation of exquisite lighting compositions, the degree of elaboration being determined by the equipment available. (See Frontispiece.)

CHAPTER 14

SUGGESTIONS FOR CINEMA CURTAIN EFFECTS

THE imaginative nature of cinema performances lends itself to lighting showmanship. Good use can be made of the delightful effects obtained on stage draperies by the correct use of colour lighting.

LIGHTING ON CINEMA CURTAINS

It is now general practice to lead into a feature picture by opening the curtains to reveal the cinema screen and to light both curtains and screen in coloured lights. Lighting is maintained on the screen for the duration of the titles, and appropriate colour hues are chosen in line with the type of story that is to be unfolded. The curtains are closed on the screen at the end of the picture and are again illuminated with coloured light of a suitable hue.

Stage curtains are generally opened and closed on more than one occasion during each performance and in the case of an interval will remain closed for a short period. By means of lighting they can be given a different appearance on each occasion, and during an interval the lighting can be constantly changing in colour so that the curtains have a considerable entertainment value.

There is an art of presentation, involving individual showmanship, and stage draperies and colour lighting are the means by which films are visually introduced in most cinemas. Stage presentations including live artists are sometimes employed to introduce a feature picture, but even then the visual effect will depend largely on draperies, lighting, and showmanship. Other parts of the programme will probably depend entirely upon draperies and colour lighting.

EMOTIONAL EFFECT OF COLOUR

A good deal has been written concerning the psychology of colour, but no definite rules have been agreed. At present, the subject is quite open for individual interpretation: different people have their own ideas concerning the feelings aroused by different colours. The writer has given some thought to this subject and the following notes, resulting from a series of experiments, may be of interest. The experiments in question were carried out on a colour lighted background to a cinema screen, the purpose being to ascertain which colour of light is most suited to different occasions. The conclusions were as follows—

Red	Danger
Orange	Warmth and excitement
Sun Colours	Contentment
Pale Green	Kindness
Green	Macabre
Peacock Blue	Sinister
Blue	Quiet depth of feeling
Violet	Delicate emotion
Cerise	Deep affection
Lavender	Wistfulness

It will be appreciated that these suggestions concern luminous colour and not coloured fabrics and surfaces. Colour lighted areas often have a quality that is lacking in painted and dyed surfaces: violet, for example, is a much more beautiful hue in luminous colour.

It is important to choose colour lighting that is emotionally correct when leading into or rounding off a feature film. For example, the opening titles of a sinister film story should be lighted in green or greenish-blue light, rather than in yellow or pink. Changes in the hue of the lighting should have continuity of purpose and properly lead to the right effect for the opening of the story. At the end of the film, the minds of the audience will be stirred in a certain way, and here again the lighting, as the story closes, should be emotionally correct and should lead into the next feature on the programme—whether this is another film or " God Save the King."

SELECTION OF COLOURS

It is fairly general practice to light both cinema screen and curtains from top and bottom in different colours, as this adds to the beauty of effect. In choosing lighting for a specific mood, however, it is wise not to use widely contrasting colours from top and bottom or the suggestive value of the lighting will be reduced: rather, the colours should be closely related to each other. Thus, if green-blue (peacock) is required to create a sinister effect, the complementary colour of red, while creating a beautiful arrangement, will balance out and destroy the suggestive power of the peacock blue. Instead, the second colour should be a near colour to the green-blue, i.e. a bluish or greenish hue. Generally it is better for the second colour to be a near colour that is closer to blue in the spectral order of colours.

A contrasting hue of light, however, can be used without destroying the suggestive value of the main lighting if it covers a small area only. Thus, stage draperies, lighted in peacock blue from the footlights and blue from an overhead batten, may be given a tinge of orange light across the folds from some equipment in the wings. The contrasting colour, however, must be subdued and not cover too large an area or it will balance out the other colours.

Complementary colours together make white light and therefore indicate completeness. They provide a maximum colour contrast, but if seen quite separately are apt to create rather too strong an effect. Thus, green and mauve, yellow and blue, red and peacock blue colours, if seen jointly but separately, are vivid colour arrangements. If, however, the two colours merge into each other over part of the area of the curtain, then the sharp separation between the two hues is lost, and instead they are linked together by the gradation of tones in the area of merged colour. This is particularly true in the case of festoon curtains. (See Plate V.)

When contrasting colours are to be seen separately and distinctly, it is often better to choose colours that, while quite different in hue, have one primary colour in common. Thus, instead of green and mauve, the colours would be peacock blue and mauve (when blue is common to both colours), or perhaps yellow and mauve (when red is common to both colours). The primary colour common to both hues should be present in the same strength in each case: in the case of violet and yellow-green, red would be present only in a small degree in the yellow-green, leaving green as the predominant hue of this colour, while violet, of course, has very little red.

The colour circle shown in Fig. 65 is a useful guide for the choice of complementary colours, and the colour circles in Figs. 66 and 67 to contrasting colours. Pleasing combinations of contrasting hues can be made by choosing colours that are equally distant from each other around the colour circle.

LIGHTING THE CURTAINS

Proscenium curtains on a cinema stage are usually only lighted by the footlights, and there is little opportunity to provide contrasting effects. However, proscenium curtains can sometimes be set back a little so that vertical proscenium battens at each side of the stage can throw contrasting light across the folds of the curtains.

Screen curtains are usually well back from the footlights, and are generally lighted also from overhead batten equipment. The lighting from these two directions generally merges over a large area, so that very sharp contrasts are not obtained. Excellent contrast effects can usually be achieved if efficient spotlights or floodlights are employed at the sides of the stage, as the vertical folds of the curtain can be sharply caught without the light merging into the general illumination.

A much greater variety of effect can be achieved if curtains are lighted from the sides as well as from top and bottom, and the additional cost is well worth while. Alternatively, it is better to light curtains from the bottom and from the sides rather than from top and bottom, whenever this is possible. Top and bottom lighting will illuminate a curtain from two directions only, but lighting from sides and bottom is coming from three directions. If both sets of wing equipment are controlled on the same circuits, only the same amount of control apparatus is required. It is also possible to arrange the colour filters in the wing equipment so that opposite sides light up in contrasting colours, although controlled by the same dimmers.

Cinema stage lighting equipment should always be arranged for circuits of red, green, and blue light, with each circuit controlled by its own dimmer. As shown in Chapter 1, red, green, and blue are primary colours, and when combined in different proportions will enable almost every known hue of colour to be obtained. White light can be provided by the use of red, green, and blue circuits together. This is suitable for curtain effects, but it is wise to have a fourth circuit of white light available if the stage is used frequently for acting purposes, because the three-colour white is a little lower in intensity, and the presence of an ordinary white circuit may be useful.

Sometimes cinema theatres have stage equipment for the presentation of elaborate production numbers, and in these cases, considerable use is usually made of draped settings. Very beautiful colour lighting effects are then possible, because lighting can be thrown on to the curtains from many directions, and the lighting changed in hue, as desired. It is important that the acting area should be lighted independently, so that artists on the stage do not have to be illuminated in the colours used for the illumination of the setting. Overhead spot battens are very useful for this purpose. Additional spotlights located at the sides of the stage and auditorium can also help in the acting area illumination. It is important, however, that these spotlights should light the stage at an angle, so that there is little or no interference with the colour lighting effects on the draped setting and surround.

CURTAIN MATERIALS

Very shiny curtain materials are not always the most suitable for lighting effects, because, if they are located too near to the equipment, there is a tendency for streaky effects to arise, with poor merging of the primary colour circuits. Satin drapes are effective when located at a distance from the lighting apparatus, but if in close proximity are too specular in their reflection. Silk velour is an excellent material from a lighting viewpoint, but care must be taken to use the material with the pile brushing in the right direction. To get the best illuminated effect, the pile should brush away from the lighting equipment. This means that proscenium curtains lighted only by the footlights should be made with the pile running in the direction opposite to that normally employed, i.e. the pile should lie down when brushed in an *upward* direction. The curtain will then gleam and give the best possible illumination effect, whereas, with the pile in the opposite direction, the curtain will appear dull except at the very bottom.

Border cloths and leg curtains should be constructed of material that adequately masks adjacent lighting equipment. Frequently, this means that the material must be lined, because satin or sateen, for example, will light up from the back and reveal the presence of lighting equipment. Many people employ black velour curtains for borders and leg curtains, so that the lighting effects are seen at their best on the actual stage curtains, and attention is not distracted by over-bright illumination of the masking draperies.

INDEX

195

THEATRE AND STAGE
SERIES

General Editor: **HAROLD DOWNS**

PITMAN